Ocean of Ideas and Inspiration for Writers

Prolific Writing for Everyone, Volume 9

Warren Brown

Published by Warren Brown, 2023.

While every precaution has been taken in the preparation of this book, the publisher assumes no responsibility for errors or omissions, or for damages resulting from the use of the information contained herein.

OCEAN OF IDEAS AND INSPIRATION FOR WRITERS

First edition. November 15, 2023.

ISBN: 979-8223854012

Written by Warren Brown.

Also by Warren Brown

Prolific Writing for Everyone
Universe of Creativity and Inspiration for Writers
Ocean of Ideas and Inspiration for Writers
On Writing Magic
The Writer's Creativity Cave
The Writer's Oasis
Castle of Ideas and Inspiration for Writers
Chasm of Creativity and Inspiration For Writers
Island of Creativity and Inspiration for Writers

Standalone
Supernova: A Collection of Science Fiction Short Stories
Instant Poetry App
The Power of the Storyteller- A Collection of Short Stories
Vintage Tales: Eurasian Short Stories
Impostor Assassin
Camelot Crypto 1- Crypto Genesis
Camelot Crypto 2- Crypto Odyssey
Camelot Crypto 3- Crypto Symbiosis
Camelot Crypto: Three Short Crypto-currency Stories
Three Christmas Coins: A Poem
The Christmas Dimension

Watch for more at https://warren4.wixsite.com/warren.

Table of Contents

Ocean of Ideas and Inspiration for Writers

Prolific Writing for Everyone- Book 9

By
Warren Brown

Introduction

There is a famous 11th century collection of stories, folktales, legends and histories written in Sanskrit, by the Shaivite Somadeva, called the "Kathasaritsagara" or the "Oceans of the Streams of Stories". There are multiple layers of story, within a story in this amazing collection of stories. The "Kathasaritsagara", is a large collection of stories loosely strung together. The stories are narrated for the recreation and the information of the same individual or stories about their adventures.

This book that you are reading right now is the "Ocean of Ideas and Inspiration for Writers" and it is a collection of several poems, articles and stories which contain nuggets of ideas for writers, to develop.

Every story, article or poem in this book, can be compared to an oyster in the ocean, that has the seed of a good idea, you as the writer can use to create a wonderful story. These stories are the product of the imagination and creativity of the author. You as a writer can use these ideas to inspire you to become a prolific writer.

I have completed and published over 3000 stories, articles and poems on Medium, the publishing platform. I have also over the past two decades written and published over 200 books on Amazon.

I would like to encourage you as a writer to create and share your stories, articles and poems for the world to enjoy. If you enjoy writing as much as I do, you will have the strong desire to keep writing your ideas. It is important to keep a journal filled with your ideas. It is also necessary to develop the habit of writing every day.

The "Ocean of Ideas and Inspiration", is waiting for you to dive into today and to unleash the tidal waves of creativity to create your own work.

Thank you for purchasing this book and I am sure that you will enjoy reading it and using the writing tips, ideas to inspire you on the Writer's Way, today and every day of your life. Share your talent with the world as a writer and always know that writing is your contribution to the literary field and it is your legacy.

Your Writing Friend

Warren Brown

Writing Prompt: How does it feel creating a Sea of content?

Just fifty stories would be the beginning of a sea and a thousand an Ocean

Have you started creating your sea of content? A collection of ten stories could be your first literary sea drop, a hundred could be a puddle of water, while 500 would be a pond, 1000 stories a sea and 5,000 stories an ocean of literary work. This is just a hypothetical statement and it is meant to inspire and motivate the writer within you.

I have been writing since January 2021 and have crossed 2,800 stories in September 2023. I write almost every day, a variety of pieces that include, poetry, articles and stories. The theme of ninety-percent of my writings is about the art and craft of writing, fiction and poetry, and very few of my pieces are related to statistics, how to blog and how to earn an income. A large proportion of my work is fiction, as it gives me an opportunity to use my imagination and creativity.

Are you a writer who has completed a minimum of ten stories on a publishing platform, and you are eager to write more stories poems and articles? You must be feeling very excited and rightfully so, as you are gradually creating your own sea of content. Always remember that your writings are your intellectual property and you can publish your collected works as an e-book and in other online and offline publications as well. Your content can also be converted into video presentations on YouTube is you desire. Own your content, by reproducing it on your blog as well or create a course.

Congratulations, if you have completed fifty stories, articles and poems. You are definitely on your way to making your sea of literary content. Tell the world about your work and spread the news on social media. If you are enthusiastic about writing and passionate about your subjects, then it is time to share your creation with the world.

How do you feel creating your sea of content? Is it a challenge for you or do you plan to slowly but surely write a poem, article or story a day? Not because you must write, but because you enjoy writing and it is a pleasure creating your own work and lovingly generating your own content for you to use as you wish in the future.

I love writing and creating my literary works, so it is not a chore for me, to write almost every day of the year. If you truly love writing, you will know what I mean. A dedicated writer can change the world with his or her positive writings in a very powerful and positive way, as words and images are the brain's tools of constructive power.

Prompt: How long have you been away from the Sea?

Who can forget the movies where the sea is the landscape and the setting for the story, like "Titanic", "20, 000 Leagues under the sea", "The Poseidon Adventure", "Juggernaut" and so many others? All these stories take place on the sea in cruise liners and they are filled with thrills and great adventures. The characters have to face difficult issues and solve large conflicts, all the while having the sea present, with its calm and violent moments. If you have not seen these movies, perhaps you should, even if you are not too fond of movies and stories about the sea like "Moby Dick".

There are many who have not seen the sea in reality, all they have seen are movies where the sea is the setting for a story or they have read descriptions about the sea in essays, novels and poems. I am fortunate to have visited the seaside several times and it is an exhilarating experience to witness the beauty, the ferocity and the majesty of a large body of water, that seems so limitless.

How long has it been for you since you last visited the sea and would you go back to visiting it once again, and why would you visit? If I do go back to the seaside to see the sea in all its glory, it will be because of the experience. Although the sea appears to be just a large body of water, it is teeming with so many lifeforms, that all lie within it, yet it appears to be so plain and clear on the surface, except for a few fish, whales, plants and walruses that appear here and there.

The sea reminds me of the human mind with a few impressions that appear on its surface, during its day-to-day interactions, yet, the unconscious mind is brimming with ideas, that are available to every creative mind.

Writing Prompt: Are you a Casual Writer or a Lifelong Writer?

Some people write a poem or a story once a week. Some write a poem once a month, while some write a poem, or story or an article every day. There are some writers who write a minimum of two to three articles or poems a day. Always remember that the writer who writes three articles a day did not start off in that way, he or she started by writing one poem or story a day. Sometimes it takes a decade or two, before a writer is able to compose and publish three literary pieces a day.

Are you a casual writer, who writes whenever you feel the need to express yourself? This is okay if you are not really serious about becoming a writer. Are you a person who is serious about taking up the writing craft and making it a lifelong hobby or career? Then you need to write every day, rain, snow or sunshine, regardless of whether you feel like writing or not. After a while, writing a literary piece a day will become as natural as breathing. It is at that time, when you as a writer will feel that writing one piece a day is not enough, as you still have so much to say, because the ideas will seemingly appear out of thin air.

What is your motivation for choosing the writer's path, is it money of fame or do you want to express yourself and share your ideas with the world? If it is fame and fortune you seek, then the literary craft is not for you. Unless you are an extraordinary writer, who has strong connections with literary agents and publishing houses.

However, if you are like me, and you are truly passionate about writing, regardless of the money you earn from it and you do not feel that writing is a chore, then I heartily welcome you to the Writer's path. Writing every day will help you to improve your literary skills. I am here to help and guide writers on the literary way, with my ideas, thoughts and suggestions. I am a lifelong writer and will continue to write every day as it is in my genes and it is who I am as an individual in the world and this is my legacy and contribution to human civilization. Our words may be forgotten and we may be forgotten with the passage of time, but think of all the souls you have helped entertain as a writer over the years.

How Many Coins Do you put into the Fountain Every Day? I put in Three Coins

We all throw coins into the fountain of wishes every day, whether we know it or not and whether we want to or not. I try to put a minimum of three coins into the fountain every day. These are not really gold or silver coins, unlike the fountains you may have heard of over the years, where people throw in three coins to make wishes come true.

Every positive task that you do is a coin of positivity. I try my best to do something positive every day and so collect my coins from the Universal Cosmic Bank of Unlimited Wealth. How do you find positive things to do? That is simple, when you see something that needs to be done, do it without making a fuss. When you spot someone who needs a helping hand or some advice or someone to speak to, take you time to help them out, without making a public display of yourself for the world to notice. Believe me, these small yet significant acts of positivity, will help you to collect coins of positive power, which you can visually imagine yourself throwing into the wishing fountain. You do not even need to state your wishes, as your deepest desires are known by the cosmic forces that lie within us and outside us at all times.

My favourite method for collecting coins of positive power is by writing poems, articles or stories that have positive vibes. Almost every literary piece that I create I fill with positive power to inspire and motivate readers and other writers. I write about three pieces a day and so as a bonus to my every day activities, I collect three additional positive power coins to throw into my Fountain of Wishes. It does not take too long, before your wishes start coming true. Begin collecting and depositing your positive wishing coins into the Universal Cosmic Bank of Unlimited Wealth today. By writing this article, I have collected my fourth wishing coin today.

Are You a Prospector for Great Opportunities?

We hear of people getting good opportunities out of the blue, while there are some who never seem to get any great opportunities in life. We often ask ourselves the same question, why is it difficult for me to find awesome opportunities in life? On the other-hand there are some really lucky individuals who get scores of golden opportunities coming their way almost all the time.

Are you a prospector of golden opportunities? If you are then you are working with the cosmic forces of creation and you know the secret of making great things come your way. The word prospector made me think of the California gold rush of 1848 to 1855 and the prospectors going to find gold, while living in wretched conditions. All the prospectors went hunting for nuggets of gold from the goldmines hoping to find a fortune to change their miserable lives and to help their families. They carried hope in their hearts, though many did not survive.

However, you can be a prospector and discover great opportunities in life, by looking in the right places. It is essential to use the power of gratitude in your heart and you will find that amazing opportunities come to you out of nowhere. Be grateful for all that you have in life and share your happiness with others, by doing good things for others. This sharing of the power of gratitude in the world, will help you to become a prospector of fantastic opportunities for your life.

The Burden of Memories

Our minds can get confused,
        When we have so many memories.
They are so powerful and alive,
Like so many great stories.
We carry our memories with us,
Every day, we remember them.
Every day, we can feel those memories,
Those powerful long-lost stories.
The burden of our memories,
Can get heavier as the years go by.
Can we toss all those memories away?
We know we will be free of them someday.
Memories can be so very precious.
Our minds record every memory,
Into our souls and within our hearts.
Your life story is locked in your memory.

She did not believe in Fairy tales

L ife was always difficult for her,
 Nothing was easy for her to do.
There were always obstacles in the way,
There were challenges to be faced every day.
Heather did not believe in fairy tales,
Fairies, goblins, princes and killer whales.
She was very realistic about her life,
She was used to anguish and strife.
The girl did not believe in fairy tales,
Till her life started to grow and change.
Good fortune seemed to smile on her,
Her life and vision were now crystal clear.
Heather did not believe in fairy tales,
Till she got work as a photographer.
She clicked so many happy times of joy,
She had a life no one could destroy.
As a young woman she started to believe,
That a fairy tale does happen for everyone.
She met the man of her dreams one fine day,
A baby son was later born to them in May.

Jon Gave Himself to the A.I. Matrix

Artificial intelligence was sweeping the world, it was transforming every known and unknown industry in the history of mankind. Jon was fascinated with this new type of science, where the impossible was now possible. It was now possible to create videos out of photographs, he could convert his text to speech and he could create movies using virtual environments. A.I. made it possible for him to generate project reports and to get virtual assistance for all the work he needed to do. Jon created products using A.I. and he had a virtual sales force working for him night and day, to ensure his millionaires lifestyle in every way.

As a gift to the Gods of A.I. he decided to gift his brain to the science of A.I. when it was time for him to die. In his reality he was lost and lonely, yet in his virtual avatar, he was surrounded with friends and colleagues, who were in touch with him. Jon was a prosperous man, he never found true love during his life time. Jon spent so much time in the matrix of A.I., that he decided to gift himself, his body and his brain to advancing the field of artificial intelligence.

Jon is now living in the matrix of A.I. every day and night, with an eternity of a future that looks really bright. He does not need to eat, sleep or rest, his life seems alive and so much better than before, he could not dream or ask for more. A.I. is making Jon's dreams come true, he loves it like a broken curio loves superglue. Jon has learned all the smartest tricks to make his virtual life so much fun, he is well ahead of every human, living under the Sun.

Is Jon really happy? He still feels lonely at times, when he misses human company. "No man is an Island!", is so true and we all need human interaction in our daily lives. Though, A.I. can help humans to live forever in a digital world, once their life on Earth is done.

Stars in Heaven- They shine so brightly in Eternity

They shine and sparkle every day and night,
    A most beautiful vision to behold.
The stars shine with their starry light,
Brightly they gleam for the Creator's sight.
Every loved one we lose from Earth,
Is born as a star in the Heavenly sky.
They are blessed with peace and eternity,
A gift from the cosmic Creator on high.
Shine so brightly loved ones,
Who look down on us every day.
Though you are gone and not here,
We know that we will meet someday.
Stars in Heaven shining with love,
Shine your light from up above.
We are together though we are apart,
In the Chapel in the forest of our heart.
Poet's Note: Dedicated to the memories of my mother, Joan Brown, who passed away on the 10th of August 2018 and to my father, Melvyn Brown, who passed away on the 25th of June 2023.

A Memoir as a Vault of Memories- Every page filled with emotions

When we think of a vault, we think of banks, security guards, iron, steel, large doors, with complex locking systems, digital and cryptic keys. However, when we talk about a memoir, we are talking about a person opening their heart to us, within the covers of a book. Famous, infamous, ordinary or a common person, their story is told within the delicate pages of a book, or digitally produced as an e-book. Actor, singer, writer, banker, doctor, or crook, their thoughts and experiences in life are stored in a simple and fragile book.

A memoir is a vault of precious memories that have been gathered by the writer. Each memory holding a special place in their life and in their heart, each being an integral part of their lives and personalities. When you read a memoir, you can feel every tiny emotion emanating from the pages. Every life story, written by the writer in great detail, makes it so interesting to read.

A memoir is a storehouse of so many things, from a person's life, that include their young days, their school and college days, right through the time they stepped out into the world, to the time they made a name for themselves in society, with all their joys, sorrows, failures, loves and triumphs till they reach their twilight years. The writer of a memoir invites you to observe their life, and to learn from their mistakes and to read about the wisdom they have gained over the years. Think about writing your memoir today, it could be your bestseller.

Gaining Inspiration and Motivation from Memoirs

The time you broke your hand, the time you made a fool of yourself at your friend's wedding, the time you missed having a major accident, the time you mistook an unknown woman to be your girlfriend, the time you missed your lunch date, these are just a few of the memories that you could include in your memoir. You have more exciting ones to include in your memoir, I am sure.

Write down a list of all the pleasant and unpleasant memories that you have had in life. After you have made a list of them, write about each experience in great detail. Make every incident either happy, sad or just embarrassing, depending on how you felt at the time, as far as you can remember. The emotions that you bring to the surface in each story, will keep the reader engrossed, and it will make your memoir a page-turner.

Create a list of all the wisdom that you have gained over the years as a result of your life experiences. After you have made a list of these nuggets of wisdom, develop them for inclusion in your memoir. Why do people read memoirs? It is to know how ordinary as well as successful people have lived their lives.

Every memoir that has ever been written gives the reader an opportunity to catch a glimpse of the mind, and life experiences of the author. Sometimes, a reader may find that there are a few events that are similar to the one he or she has experienced. This makes the reader sympathetic to the writer and more interested in reading the whole story from start to finish. Readers generally get inspired and motivated after reading memoirs. Write your page-turning memoir starting today.

We are the Faces of Creation

The world is our stage to live and play,
  To make the most of every passing day.
This world is here for us to stay,
To learn, to love and live every day.
We are the faces of creation.
We are the souls that are chosen,
To spend our lives on this planet.
To thrive on this world and return to it.
We are the cosmic beings of creation,
We are here to fail, learn and to win.
On this world we live our cosmic destinies,
Just like the plants, the bees and the trees.
The world is our revolving stage,
Each day lived is an Act completed.
This world is ours and we call it home,
Our destinies are fulfilled as we live and roam.

Your Boundless Imagination- Set it Free Today

C an you imagine a world where people use the power of their imagination to make their lives so much richer, so much brighter and their lives so much simpler? Your imagination has no limits, there are no boundarics to how far you can imagine, to how much creativity you can express, to what you can create with your mind.

Your mind is shackled by all the limitations that have been placed on you in this world. Those heavy chains of what cannot be done, what cannot be imagined and what cannot be created get heavier every day and they gain strength when you give in and do nothing.

The instant that you decide to use the power of your imagination, the limitless power of your creativity, you begin to break those golden chains encircling your powerful mind. Your boundless imagination needs to be released and allowed to grow and evolve through your life, what you create and in everything that you do in life starting from today.

Even the simplest tasks in life, can be made to feel like fun when you put your mind to it and look at the work more creatively and give in to your powers of imagination. Never be embarrassed to use your creativity and imagination in whatever work that you do. Your creativity, could be the creation of something new, something simpler and an invention that could change your world.

This is the world in which we presently live where people can use the power of their limitless creativity to change their lives in an effective and positive way. Start using your boundless imagination today it is an untapped source of power. It can be your superpower, to make a difference in the world and in your life.

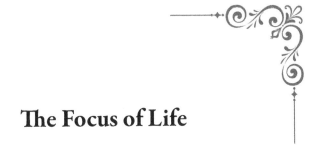

The Focus of Life

If the focus of your life is money, luxuries, fame and fortune, then you will definitely achieve it soon. If the focus of your life is good health, then after following a good diet and healthy living you will achieve that goal. If the focus of your life is to be a great athlete, then after years of training, your prowess as an athlete will help you to maintain peak performance in your sport.

What was the focus of your life a few years ago and has it changed? It is possible that a few years ago, you had different dreams and ambitions. Those dreams have since been replaced by newer ones. What is the focus of your life today, is it your job, your family or your hobby? It is possible that you are now giving a lot of time to the subject of your focus in your life today. This is helpful, because the causes that we focus on in life today, can make a huge difference to us, our lives and it can benefit your community too.

What will be the focus of your life be tomorrow. Will it be something else or you have not yet decided on it? Here is a suggestion. Make the focus of your life for the future, to be the most important individual of this life and that person is you. If you are going to be a person to make a difference in life, for yourself, your friends, family, community and society, then you need time to focus on yourself.

You should put time aside for meditation, self -development, spirituality to get in touch with who you are inside, the invisible part of you that resides deep within. Take the time to nourish, your mind, body and your soul. It is only when you have evolved as a positive individual, can you be an agent for positive change in the world. The focus of your life plays an important part in how you feel every day.

The Silent and Powerful
Art of Graffiti

When I am on the train watching the city pass me by, I see a lot of graffiti, here, there and everywhere. In London you can find a few graffiti displays, on the sides of buildings, down lanes and along walls that are close to the train lines, there are also trains that get dressed in colourful graffiti. It is sometimes amazing to see the spots in which these graffiti appear. How could anyone go to that part of the wall that is so close to the underground train tunnel and paint a piece of graffiti? How could anyone paint a piece of graffiti across the side of the bridge? The artist must have been precariously balancing himself or herself to create that artistic piece.

Graffiti artists are gifted and allow themselves to create their art, that comes from their hearts and speaks volumes to us as observers. There are powerful messages in the graffiti that you see, looking at the world in satire, observing the fun and the politics, sending messages of freedom and peace. If you were a graffiti artist, what message would your graffiti contain? What do you think about the silent, colourful and powerful art of graffiti?

Holidays for Soul Happiness

I f you are ever offered a holiday,
   Take it without complaining too much.
A holiday can make you feel much better,
It can fill your heart and make your vision clear.
A holiday is just what the Doctor ordered.
Go and have fun with family and friends.
Holiday enjoyment never truly ends.
It can sometimes drive you around the bend.
A holiday will make you shine,
It will make you relax and smile.
Walk away from the work and grime,
Enjoy your holiday and have fun this time.
Holidays nourish your heart and warms the soul,
It binds you to those you love, making you whole.
Everyone deserves a holiday in life,
A short break to love and enjoy life.

Gazing at the Lotus Pond- A beautiful sight to behold

The lotuses were blossoming,
        In the tranquil waters of the pond.
    The cool air wafted across the waters,
    The perfume of the open flowers,
    Was carried in the air to sons and daughters.
    It moved across the gardens and the trees,
    In that soft and gentle scented breeze.
    She looked at the lotus pond,
    She felt joy within her heart.
    Slowly she knelt to touch the water,
    As the perfume of the flowers,
    And their beauty touched her.
    Gazing at the lotus pond,
    Is a beautiful sight to behold?
    In nature there is so much beauty,
    That we can cherish and hold,
    Within our hearts and in our minds,
    A moment with nature as it lovingly binds.
    She held the waters in her hand,
    It was a moment so lovely and divine.
    Nature blessed her at the lotus pond,
    With a cool whisper like a magic wand.

When nature speaks, we should listen,
We hear it in our beating hearts within.

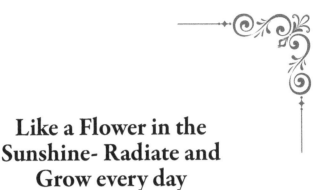

Like a Flower in the Sunshine- Radiate and Grow every day

After the rains, the soil is watered and the gardens seem to come alive. It is only when the sunshine starts that we see a garden starting to grow and thrive. Every crop in a farmer's field gives forth its yield, when it is watered well throughout the year and it is bathed in the warmth of sunshine.

A city can look dreary, old and battered when it is lives through every busy day. It is only after the dwellers in a city start to take care of it that it begins to come alive once again. Buildings are painted, streets are repaired, money is spent and responsibilities are shared. Everyone starts to take care of their city.

Like a flower in the sunshine, it is time to radiate and grow every day. Some days can be dull and grey, while other days can be filled with positivity and joy. There are busy days at work, while there are fun days with friends and family. There are the memorable days like birthdays, graduations, weddings, new born arrivals and anniversaries. Take the sunshine of every day and add the positivity into your life. Keep the sunshine stored for use on those dull and gloomy days.

Today is a day filled with sunshine. Take all the sun that you can, to store away in your mind, heart and soul. It is time for you to radiate your sunshine to the world, to become an agent of positive changes in society. Branch out like a tree and spread your warm sunshine and radiate your glow, wherever you wander and wherever you may go in life.

Short Story- Always in a Box- No way of getting out

He was a busy man, he was always doing something in his life, yet he was a lonely man. He was Jerry the man who had so many jobs to do in his life, sometimes he was a soldier, some days he was a policeman, some days he was a fireman and there were days when he was just out in the sunshine not doing anything. Regardless of the activities or his mood, he was always put away in a box, at the end of the day. There was no way that he was getting out.

There was so much that Jerry wanted to do with his life. Yet, at the end of the day, he was put away and he was so lonely. Jerry was a toy in a young boy's toy box. The youngster would take him out every morning and place him with all the other toys. After school the young child would play with all his toys. Sometimes he made Jerry the soldier, some days he became the policeman. On days when the boy wanted to run around with his fire-engine, Jerry became the fireman. On other days, when the child wanted to play with his superhero toys, he would keep Jerry aside. At the end of every day, the young Tom would place Jerry into his small toy box, that was specially made for him, he was the boy's prized possession.

This story reminds me of all of us in life. We work, we love, we live and we play, till we are old and grey. We go home at the end of the day, there is no more to do, say or play. Later in life, we retire from the hectic life of work, work, work and spend time living comfortably in the sun, if that is possible, with costs rising and people working till the bitter end. At the end of our lives, we break free from the "toy box", called life.

Dream-making- The Dreams of Yesterday

Yesterday we had so many dreams,
    About what we would do with our time,
We even wrote it down in verse and rhyme,
About where we would go in life.
A lot of dreams with a lot of hopes.
Some dreams we follow,
While some we forget.
The dreams of yesterday,
Do we follow them anyway?
Today is the time to start,
Making those dreams come true.
You deserve to have those dreams come true,
That is your right and it is your due.
You are the dream maker of your dreams,
Create those dreams in realities today,
This is your life fill it with your real dreams.
We worry that dreams may not come true.
We are hesitant to start working towards,
Those elusive and hazy dreams.
If you have visions of what you want in life,
Start working towards that destination today.
This is your life and your destiny pathway.
Tomorrow is too far away,

Dream and live your dreams today.
Make your dreams a reality starting today,
This life is your life, so do it your way.
You are the Dream and the Maker of Dreams,
Live your dreams in every possible way.
Your dreams of yesterday are a reality today.

Every Piece is a Spark of Emotion- Every thought is a shiny Gemstone

A writer keeps imagining, creating and writing, without stopping. He or she is relentless in his or her pursuit of the muse, who keeps supplying him or her with all the ideas necessary to create literary pieces. An artist does not question all the ideas that seem to come from nowhere into his or her mind. The artist faithfully keeps producing the work for the world to admire and to enjoy.

Likewise, a songwriter keeps putting words to all the wonderful melodies that come into his or her mind. As writers we are all so familiar with the feeling of "where did that idea come from?" Yet, we know that the ideas that seem to come from the ether actually originate from within ourselves. The ideas that we produce in our literary presentations are exciting combinations of our life experiences, our emotions, our imagination and our creativity.

Every piece of writing that a writer produces represents a spark of his or her emotions. Within every creative piece of work, is a shiny gemstone of a thought. When a writer creates a substantial number of literary pieces, he or she has literally built a foundation of his or her thoughts, for the world to read, absorb and enjoy.

Remember the next story, poem, article, play, song or research piece of work that you write is just another brick in your literary foundation. It is this literary structure that has arisen from your mind, emotions and creativity, that will entertain generations of the future. You will be remembered by the words and the stories that you have told, like a seed that has been planted it will sprout into a tree of entertainment, wisdom and learning.

The Burning Sun of August

Today is a dull and cloudy day,
    Not unusual for a day in August,
In the city of London.
Yet, we know that the Sun,
Will come out soon as it does.
Today is not a hot and sunny day,
Like it could be in the month of May.
The burning Sun on a hot summer's day,
Sheds its warmth across the cities, the streets,
Drying in the breeze, wet sheets,
On all the countries of the world.
Summer comes to different places,
At various times throughout the year.
If you enjoy summer and the warm sunshine,
Keep following the Sun on its long journey,
Across continents, while eating cheese,
And sipping on cool white and red wine.
The burning Sun of August,
Reminds us that this moment is fleeting.
We need to take opportunities,
When we catch a glimpse as they shine.
A great new opportunity,
Could disappear like sunshine.

The burning Sun of August,
Needs to be welcomed with open arms,
Like a great personality with all its charms.
I hope you enjoy your radiant moment,
As you bask in your August Sunshine.
Live a life of peace, happiness and joy,
Eating cheese and sipping sweet wine.

How do you want to be remembered? As a person who did something or nothing

Yes, most people want to be remembered, no one actually wants to be forgotten in life, after they have gone. Yet, there are some people who want to be remembered as having done a lot in life, while there are those who do not want to be remembered. There are some people today, who are just concerned about themselves and their lives, while ignoring their family and spending more time with their friends, how do they want to be remembered?

Okay, no one is really forgotten in life, because we always live in the hearts and minds of our family members, friends and colleagues. What is your legacy? Is it all the work that you did during your lifetime, is it for all the projects that you did to help others or is it something else that you did to contribute to the betterment of society?

Personally, I know that life continues after a person passes away and he or she is remembered for a short period of time, for all they did during their lifetime. However, that person, who was loved by his or her friends and family, will be long remembered in the minds of hearts of those they knew, like my dad, who passed away two months ago and my Mum who passed away fifteen years ago.

During my lifetime, I want to be known for the ideas, stories and poems, I have created and shared with the world. It does not matter to me, if I am remembered or forgotten by the world, after I am gone.

There are so many souls in this life and we all have a part to play. What matters most to the world is what we do in the present and how we work together to make the world a better place to live for ourselves and all who we interact with in life. How do you want to be remembered?

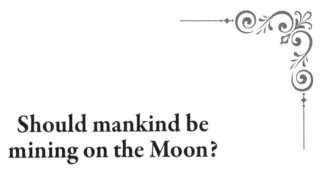

Should mankind be
mining on the Moon?

There will be no peace for the man on the moon, when companies start their mining operation. NASA has announced that mining operations will be starting on the moon very soon. https://www.jpl.nasa.gov/infographics/the-lunar-gold-rush-how-moon-mining-could-work

The moon holds hundreds of billions of dollars of untapped resources. Private companies are now planning a lunar economy. https://www.space.com/moon-mining-gains-momentum

There will be a lot of "blowing up" areas on the moon, where minerals are detected. A number of the materials that will be extracted from the Moon are oxygen, water, fuel, metals to fabricate lunar housing, landing pads, along with other structures and products. At present policies, rules, regulations are being put in place, so that the creation of a lunar economy can be set into motion.

Will the mining on the moon have an adverse effect on the Earth, its gravitational pull on the waters of the Earth, its reflecting of the light from the Sun and its position in the gravitational field of the Earth, Sun and the other planets of the solar system? Time will tell, if this is a good move for humanity.

The Moon will gradually be turned into another Earth, that needs to be exploited for the use and abuse of mankind. The poet, the artist and the child cannot look at the Moon as something that is beautiful and mysterious, after a thousand miners, living in mining stations are working for twenty-four hours extracting all the minerals from its core. Does, humanity's greed know no limits, will the nations of the world, find a way to one day, extract the resources from the Sun? It may not be possible today, but maybe in the future.

What do you do, when no one listens to You?

Are you familiar with this feeling? You have a lot to say, you want to tell someone about it, yet no one will listen to you. You have just completed a big project and you want to share the news with someone, but everyone is busy and no one has the time or the patience to listen to you, among your friends and family members.

You have just heard the latest news in your favourite field, it could be in music, science, art, cooking or some other interesting hobby. However, everyone at work and at home are busy doing their own thing. If you take a microphone to tell everyone the latest news that is so important to you, people will say that you are rude and obnoxious, anyway no one really wants to hear your news.

What do you do, when no one wants to listen to you, your failures, your successes and the stuff that matters to you? At those times, always remember that the best thing to do is to write a note in your journal, write a poem, article or story about your latest news and share it with readers to enjoy. Yes, there are people who look forward to reading your literary work and they are willing to share the way that your work moves them and makes them feel. If you are a writer, you are well aware of this and if you are not a writer, start writing today and sharing the news you have for the world to read or listen to and enjoy.

Breaking Good- When bad things happen to good People

For over five decades he worked,
As a librarian in a large university.
He helped students navigate their way,
Through their research projects every day.
Yet, when Robert was old and weak,
He was taken advantage of in life,
After he lost his loving wife.
Strangers took over his daily life.
She was a nurse for over forty years,
She helped people overcome their fears.
Greta was loved by everyone at the hospital,
She was always ready for every urgent call.
Greta was mugged on the street one day,
She lost her wedding ring and her pay.
She was hit on the head with a stick of wood.
Why does the universe always break the good?
Do bad things happen to good people,
For a very good and useful reason?
Why do the forces enjoy breaking the good,
Like a saw cutting a block of good wood?

An Erased Mind is a Blank mind

After a busy day at work,
    We come home to relax.
The rest at night is what we need,
A time to relax both body and mind,
Erasing tensions of every imaginable kind.
I know that our minds do not get erased,
When we awake the next morning.
What if our minds were just a blank,
As a new day was dawning?
"Who am I", I say, yawning.
Perhaps we would also forget,
Who we were and what we did?
This would not be very good,
As the mind would be a block of wood.
We would be robots where we stood.
An erased mind would be a blank mind.
Would that help us to discover,
The working of our human mind?
To help us heal scars of any kind,
There would be no love to ever find.
Imagine if our minds were erased,
Like a chalk board every single night.
We would be without any feeling,

No one would know how to love or sing.
We would be lost without emotion and feeling.

A Cup of Coffee

A s soon as the sun rose,
    Over the wild amazon jungle,
He knew it was time,
For him to wake up.
Time to drink a refreshing cup,
Of freshly made ground coffee,
From the Coffee shop beneath the tree.
A cup of coffee,
Was just what he needed,
As he swung from tree to tree.
Gorilla Bob loved his jungle life,
There was no better place to be.
He foraged for leaves and nuts,
Throughout the day till high noon.
It was time to rest before he knew it,
The sun was high every afternoon.
Gorilla Bob awoke in the evening,
As the sun was setting in the horizon.
The air was cooler now,
He sipped his warm cup of coffee,
He meditated as he swung from tree to tree.
There was no other place he wanted to be.
Night was coming and it was getting dark,
Gorilla Bob looked over the vast expanse,

Of the Amazon jungle and the trees.
It was time to meet the elders of his tribe,
To tell tales over cups of warm coffee.

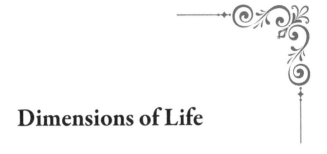

Dimensions of Life

Just as the soul can never be seen or found, similarly, life has so many dimensions that although we cannot see, do exist. We all need to fulfil our destinies by living our lives, instead of worrying about what could and could not happen. The soul is invisible and powerful, you are the bearer and the worthy carrier of that soul which needs to fulfil its earthly destiny today.

Whenever you are lost and confused in life, always remember that life can be simple but we tend to complicate things by thinking too much. My dad's favourite quote that he would like to use was "What is mind? No matter. What is matter? Never mind," for when things seemed difficult in life. Dad would tell me to slow down and to simplify the issue I was facing, by breaking it down into smaller parts. Once this was done, the problem did not seem insurmountable. This quote of my Dad, helped me to overcome several obstacles in life.

We are all aware of our mortality,
We feel that we can live forever.
Perhaps we will live forever someday,
Maybe science will find some way.
Stop every day and take a while,
To talk to somebody and smile.
Every day is a glorious gift,
Choosing happiness will give an uplift.

Being in Love and Being in Zen

The feeling of Love Zen is when you give and receive love. There is a balance between love given and love received. How and when did you have that feeling of Love Zen in your life? Love does not have to be sexual it can be spiritual. It is love that connects you with the universe and it is love that created you. It is the love for life and living that matters most. What happens when we are in that state of Love Zen and how do we feel when we have lost that feeling?

September Rain Sweet Memory

It was in the month of September,
   When he first met her on a rainy day.
It was a rainy day in September,
When he stepped out without an umbrella.
The roads were shiny and wet,
He was not even wearing a hat.
A smiling girl came up to him,
As he was soaked and so very wet.
The lovely girl gave him an umbrella,
It was a spare one she had in her bag.
She gave the umbrella to him and quickly walked away,
He was dumbstruck and never found the right words to say.
Every rainy day, he looked up and down the street,
Hoping to meet that beauty one day in the rain.
Years later he saw her as he was sitting in a bus,
She was calming her young son who was making a fuss.
Chance meetings sometimes take place in life,
They can be nothing or they can turn out to be much more.
The next time you have a lucky meeting in life,
Form a connection and it could change your life.
September rain holds such a sweet memory,
You must be having one locked away in your mind.
Go back to all the years that have come and gone,

You could have a sweet memory silently switched on.

A Long Life- Filled with marvellous stuff

Is a long life enough?
Should it be filled with marvellous stuff?
Would that even be enough?
A long life of strife and toil,
Working the land and the soil,
Would make anyone recoil.
A life filled with good deeds,
Would be a planter who scatters,
A million rich germinating seeds.
A life of plenty and filled with leisure,
With all types of sinful pleasures,
Would be filled with unseen treasures.
A long life of sorrow, sadness and pain,
One that has more losses and no gains,
Could be a life filled with spiritual gains?
What type of long life would you like?
One filled with fortune and full of gain,
One free of any form of mental and physical pain.
Is a long life enough?
Should it be filled with marvellous stuff?
Would that even be enough?

Who wants to be marvellous?

I never want to be smart and marvellous,
  I do want to accomplish my goals and ambitions,
I do want to live a long life of love, peace and happiness.
I am learning from failures and enjoying my small wins.
Most people prefer being ordinary humans,
Living lives of joy, happiness, peace and love,
Accepting what is given by the cosmic forces,
That rule the stars and our lives from above.
Reggie wanted to be a marvellous man,
He tried as best as he could to be good,
To be friends with everyone he met,
To get everything he wanted in his life,
To live a life of luxury free from strife.
Naomi lived a life of peace and calm,
With her husband and children on a farm.
Her life was simple and full of love and peace,
It was a life that she describes as a marvellous one,
As she watches every rising and setting Sun.

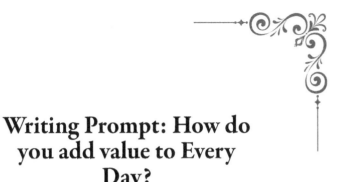

Writing Prompt: How do you add value to Every Day?

An artist adds more value to his or her day, by creating something, like a new piece of art or developing the skills to make an art piece. A sculptor adds value to his or her day, by forming an idea in his or her mind, then he or she creates a piece of work, for the world to appreciate. A poet writes a poem every day, expressing his or her deepest thoughts and desires in verse, for the world to appreciate. A doctor plays his or her part in easing the pain of patients, while a heart surgeon saves lives. They all have a role to play that impacts society in a very special way.

I enjoy creating my stories, articles and poems, every day, as it is one of the ways in which I can add value to my day, as well as to the readers who read my work. I guess that the best way to know that you are adding value to a day, is to make a day special for those you love and who work with you. I like to share my thoughts with others, while also listening to the ideas of others, as we make this journey through life.

How do you add value to every day and to your life? You will realize that by adding value to each and every day of our lives, we are also accumulating all that value over a lifetime. The value added by every individual to life has a positive impact on the world and on society. The positive value added to our world, does make massive changes to our human civilization. Every day of value, results in years and generations of positive changes to humanity.

Writing Prompt: There is not Enough Time

S orry, I cannot go there today,
    There is no time to do it tomorrow,
    Maybe, I will go over there later in the week,
    To find whatever you need and I seek.
    Do these words sound so familiar to you?
    We are all guilty of procrastinating,
    Delaying things that can be done today.
    Not doing what we should be doing anyway.
    There is not enough time in a day,
    Is what most of us like to say.
    There will be time tomorrow I am sure,
    To do what needs to be done for sure.
    Can you count the opportunities missed,
    All the great times we could have had,
    All the great people and experiences missed,
    All the lucky moments we barely kissed.
    Stop procrastinating from today,
    It is something that must be done anyway.
    Take control of every sector of your life,
    It is the best way to enjoy your life.

Writing Prompt: Are you Adaptable?

I can usually adapt to new situations in life quite easily. Whether it is getting used to a new pair of spectacles, like I am presently doing. It takes time, from the difference in the size and weight of the frames and more importantly, the power of the lenses. However, I know that I will get used to the new spectacles. Does it take you long to get used to any new gadget or accessory?

With new situations I change my mind set in order to adapt to different situations in life, like getting a new job and taking up a new project. It is important to have all the necessary tools and to acquire the required skills in order to adapt to a new situation in life. How fast do you adapt to a new course in life?

Everyone is not able to adapt to new situations in life easily. Some get used to new situations faster than others. I guess that some people are never comfortable with changes in life and with great reluctance, they are forced to accept changes, which Is stressful. I feel that the best way to adapt to new situations in life is to change your mindset. What are your opinions on change and adaptation in life?

Writing Prompt: What would you prefer, a never-ending summer or a never-ending winter?

I love the rains, the flood, the storms, not forgetting flashes of lightning lighting up the skies and the rumble of thunder. I love to see the golden rays of sunshine shining on the streets, the rooftops of houses, glistening on the shiny green leaves on tall majestic trees. I love to watch snowfall as it softly falls over the city, covering the streets, the homes, while stacking into piles on the narrowest of boundary walls, fences and even collecting on exposed pipes and statues.

What I do not love is when my hands turn dry in winter, the surface of the skin cracks and bleeds at the coldest temperatures. I dislike perspiring in summer when the temperatures rise and it does not seem like the weather will improve. I do not like it when my spectacles slide off the bridge of my nose, when it gets warm in summer. I detest wearing a sweater on a cold morning in summer, in London. The summers in Kolkata, are warmer and the rains are fiercer. I still enjoy the rains, even though the floods are severe.

The Earth is getting warmer, as the weather keeps changing and the glaciers continue to melt faster than they did before. The weather is "topsy-turvy", is what I say, and the summers are less warm, while the winters are less cold or colder sometimes. What would you prefer, a never-ending summer or a never-ending winter? Regardless of the type of weather, we have in life, or if we like or dislike it, due to global

60

warming, we need to prepare our minds for extreme weather conditions.

Writing Prompt: Indecision, should you do this or should you do that?

M aking the right decision is not easy.
  We ponder over the choices we have,
Lying in front of us almost daily.
What should we do today?
Where should we go?
We ask ourselves playfully.
Decisions, decisions, decisions.
Most people shy away from them,
While a few are unfazed by them.
What is their secret?
How can some people be so decisive?
While other lose the will to live.
Making the right decision,
Can be done with three simple questions.
Will this be good for me?
Will it help me develop as a person?
Is this the right thing to do?
Plain and honest answers to all three,
Will help you to live decisively.

Prompt: Every day is worth its weight in Gold

Is a day just another day,
    One that we can fritter away,
On doing a lot of things, or nothing?
Is a day as precious as we think?
We do know that it disappears,
In every micro-second, lost in a blink.
Every day is precious and rare,
That is what we all like to say.
Is it really so true we ask,
Is not every day filled with a task?
The tasks just multiply before us,
Which need to be done without a fuss.
Okay, so every day is worth its weight in gold,
That is what we believe and wish to be told.
There are golden moments that can fill our hearts.
Life experiences we simply cannot buy,
Yet, they raise our souls to the skies,
Loving memories that brighten our eyes.
Is there a value to every day?
Every precious moment with family,
The ones we treasure for years to come.
The comfort, love and serenity of home,
Make every day so precious and rare.

What would be the value of a day?
Happy memories, soul connections, love,
Peace, forgiveness, hope, trust and goodness,
That we nurture in our souls every passing day.

A World of Golden Opportunities

In the mind anything is possible to create

You may not know it,
   You may have heard about it,
You may not even believe it.
There is a world of golden opportunities,
It lies ahead beyond the trees and the seas.
The world of golden opportunities,
Exists in a special place in time.
That special place is so close yet so far,
Filled with beauty unseen yet filled with power.
In your mind is a world yet undiscovered,
A place where anything is possible.
In this world you can create anything,
From a palace to a dragon with silver wings.
In this world of golden opportunities,
You can create all that you desire in this world.
Act as though you are living your success,
From driving a car to wearing a designer dress.
The mind is a powerful and useful tool,
It can make all dreams come true.
The world of golden opportunities lies hidden,
Open your heart and mind to find power within.

The Opera of a Soul

There is happiness, there is sadness,
There are moments of joy,
There are moments of pain.
There are times of pleasure,
There are times of profit and gain.
One soul lives a thousand lives,
With a thousand faces to wear,
To live life without a shred of care.
A thousand lives to occupy and endure,
A thousand reasons with a magic cure.
The Opera of a Soul,
Is one that fascinates us.
Is it at all possible for one soul,
To live a thousand lives so different,
Each one lived without a trace or hint?
The opera of a soul is fun,
Filled with love and peace,
Though this is not for everyone.
There are some souls that hope and pray,
That life will change for good every day.
They forget that these are just roles we play.

In the words of my Father

I remember my dad, telling me a few years ago, that he had commented on my work, on a Facebook post he had read. However, he informed me that when he went back to view it, his comment had disappeared. I was puzzled and also thought that his reviews were lost.

Yesterday, as I was hunting for a few photos of Dad and myself on my Blog, I came across a few of Dad's reviews of my work. It was an amazing experience for me and it felt like my father was approving my literary work from across time and space, as well as informing me that he was guiding me on my Writer's Way.

Sometimes, when we feel lonely and lost after losing a loved one, we need to remember that though we cannot see them, they are still watching us and guiding us through life. My late father, Melvyn Brown, had written a review of my book, "Kingdom of Snow, a review of the short video I had made, as well as a "Happy Birthday Poem", which is awesome. Have you had a similar experience in your life, when loved ones have sent you their messages, after they have gone on their travels in eternity.

Have you seen or felt Zen Today?

Z en is the very special feeling,
  When you are at peace where you are.
When you feel comfortable and tranquil,
Wherever you are in life.
Hold onto that feeling of Zen,
Keep it with you till the count of ten.
Sitting and watching the river flow,
Looking up at the bright Sun glow,
Watching the silver light of the moon,
Listening to a flute player playing a tune.
That feeling of harmony that you feel all around,
Is a spiritual feeling so strong and powerful,
That requires no loud and boisterous sound.
Closing your eyes you feel tranquillity,
A feeling that touches the heights of serenity.
Have you seen and felt Zen today?
A harmonious vibration that is welcome any day.
That special feeling of being one with creation,
You can celebrate with Zen peace and jubilation.

Writing Prompt: Last Night I had a Lucid Dream...

L ast night I had a lucid dream,
    It was more real than I could imagine.
I was a horse rider on the vast prairies,
There were herds of wild Bisons on the green,
Moving at a fast speed across the grasslands.
The thunder of the hooves could be heard,
As the cowboys gathered the wandering herd.
Yes, it was a lucid dream I had last night,
I moved from place to place across space,
I was a traveller through dimensions and time,
Crossing continents, moving in every clime.
I was dreaming and yet I also knew,
That I was dreaming this much is true.
I moved to the land of the pyramids,
I glided into the world of the pharaohs.
I moved through the scary underworld,
Past the worlds of the ancient souls.
I saw the temple priests' worship with fires,
I saw the people offering sapphires and gold.
The lucid dream was so real to me,
I heard the voices of the living tree.
In my lucid dream journey in space and time,

I knew a million languages and every rhyme.
In my dream that was a blend of my reality,
I was a journeyman through the realms of eternity.
Every world that I passed through was just a mirror,
A reflection of so many worlds lost in time.
Yet, in my lucid dream they were as real as you and I,
With powers that enabled me to soar and to fly.
A lucid dream is more real than our reality.
I could lift the veil of our fragile humanity,
To see the power of the cosmic creator,
Who opened the doorways in the fabric of time.
The secret of this lucid dream was simple and clear,
We need to use the power of the human mind,
To cross barriers between worlds, space and time.

Writing Prompt: What is your most creative time?

Some people like to write in the morning, when the sun rises, they write at the beginning of a new day. Ideas seem to flow and creativity runs high at the start of a new day, after the mind and body have rested. The whole day lies ahead of these writers, as their imagination soars like a bird flying high in the sky. A brand-new day is celebrated every morning by these early morning writers. Are you a morning writer and feel that this is the best time to do your creative work?

A number of writers enjoy writing late at night, when the world is asleep, it allows them to think and create amazing stories and poems. The children are off to bed, the work of the day has been done, time has been spent with the family, a bit of entertainment in front of the television has been enjoyed. The mind needs a bit of rest and the best way to do it is to let those creative juices flow, as you do your best writing at night, when the moon illuminates your window and sparks your creativity. Are you a writer who enjoys writing in the evenings and at night?

I have not heard of writers, who enjoy writing during the day. I do know of writers, who make notes during the day and write their completed pieces at the end of a day. While there are a few writers who begin writing in the morning and end at midday to take a break and do their daily duties. Are you this type of midday writer?

There are times when I write at the start of the day, make notes during the day and write my literary pieces at night, especially at the weekends. I prefer to let my thoughts flow, during the course of the day, without restricting myself to writing at particular times of the day. This gives me more freedom to create my work at any time of the day, as my imagination and creativity, are not limited to any particular time during the day. What is your most creative time as a writer?

The Jinxed Shop Around the Corner

There was a small shop just around a corner,
Of a particular street in a certain neighbourhood.
Everyone called it the jinxed shop at the corner,
It was never a success, no one understood.
At first the shop was a library and bookshop,
Lending and selling books in the neighbourhood.
It was popular for a few years and things were great.
Then when the owner passed away one glorious day,
The shop was desolate and fell into a state of decay.
The shop was turned into one selling furniture,
They had the best designs in the neighbourhood.
People came from near and from far to eagerly buy,
Sofas, beds and cabinets that were not priced too high.
One dark day, there was a fire in the paint shop next door,
The flames destroyed the furniture and the shop door.
That one small shop around the corner is jinxed till today,
It has lived so many interesting lives that no one what it is today.
It has been a coffee shop, a gift shop and even a takeaway.
No one can truly say if the next shop will stay another day.

The old abandoned car

It was covered with dirt and grime,
   It had not been cleaned for a very long time.
The old car was abandoned in that yard,
Broken and rusted no one needed it,
It had done its time and was like a lost bit.
Fifty years ago, it was a brand-new car,
It belonged to a young man who loved it.
He saved his cash from his first job,
He rode it and he loved every inch of it.
The young man married and had a family.
The time came when he needed a new car.
There was no space for his three children,
His gorgeous wife who was attractive and slim.
A new car was bought that was shiny and fast,
Heads turned whenever he drove past.
Over the years the man looked at his old car,
He would definitely fix it one fine day.
The old man retired from his postal job.
He looked at his old car from his sofa every day,
He watched it looking at him with nothing to say.
The day came when the angels came for him,
He looked at his old car with a smile,
Perhaps it would be free one day too.
The man's grandson came to see the car,

He knew that it was a special kind of car.
The young man painted, soldered and polished,
Every inch of that old and battered vehicle.
The day came when the car was sparkling and new,
It was admired by all and loved by a few.
That car has a new lease of life we are told,
It drives on the road free, fast and bold.

The Gifted One

Genwin Jensen was a gifted man,
He was always working to his master plan.
He could sell snow to a man living in the snow,
He would tell stories and people asked for more.
Genwin had the gift of foresight,
He saw the future in day and night.
He was an expert at reading people,
He could control anyone with his will.
Genwin was a great speech writer,
In his time there was no one better.
His words were so powerful and strong,
He became a rich man before long.
Genwin spoke on a variety of subjects,
He could keep talking as long as the clock ticks.
Religion, politics, science and philosophy,
These were all topics he spoke on eagerly.
Genwin Jensen was a truly gifted man,
He could speak to everyone in their tongue.
Genwin was a great speaker and gifted one,
He now resides in the world beyond the Sun.

Would you travel on the Chattanooga Choo-Choo? I would

I have always loved comedies and my favourite comedians were Charlie Chaplin, Laurel and Hardy, Bud Spencer and Terence Hill. I remember the times my dad would take us to the cinema for the Saturday and Sunday matinee shows to watch some great movies. I would always be the one having a great laugh, a rip-roaring laugh, watching the slapstick antics of comedians or thoroughly enjoying the great action movies with my excited yells at the hero or the villains.

Dad knew that I loved comedies so whenever he would get a good clip-on YouTube or TikTok or Instagram, he would forward it to me on my mobile. I would watch the video and then ring my father and thank him for sending me the clip. I loved comedies, good humour, action movies, along with great rock and roll music.

A year ago, dad sent me a clip and it was a great comedy clip, but I could not remember it or find it on my phone. This evening I was searching YouTube for the video with the search keywords being, "comedy, train video, Charlie Chaplin". There it was, the "Chattanooga Choo-Choo" video with Charles Chaplin accompanied by the best comedians from the golden age of comedy, like Buster Keaton, Laurel and Hardy and a few others. You may be able to spot a few more, if you happen to like comedies too.

I would love to travel on the "Chattanooga Choo-Choo" if there were tickets available. It would be the opportunity of a lifetime to go on a train ride with so many icons of comedy. Would you take this golden opportunity to travel on the "Chattanooga Choo-Choo", if tickets were being sold today, close to where you live?

Do You Enjoy Front Row Seats?

We are given the front row seats,
    To this great experience called life.
We have the front row seats to observe,
All that happens to us and through us,
Which we do, yet we make a fuss.
The front row seats to a sport game,
Is great to watch, we are just spectators.
Looking at the sportspeople play their game,
We are present as an audience in name.
In our lives we are not just spectators,
We are the players and the observers.
Our lives our enriched as we live our lives,
As participants, from daughters, sons,
Grandparents, husbands and as wives.
Do you enjoy the front row seats,
To your own life as you live and love?
Does the experience change over time?
Is your soul quenched in poetic rhyme?
We have the front row seats to life today,
We see nature, we see life blossom in every way.
Front row seats in life does expand our mind,
Making our souls richer, peaceful and kind.

Are you living Your Dream today?

We all have those dreams in our heads,
    The ones we carry with us for years.
The dreams that are born in your heart and soul,
The ones that make you complete and whole.
There are dreams that are so impossible,
That they may never come true.
Yet, the time may come someday,
When those dreams come to you.
We would all love to live our dreams,
Those big ideas we hold in our heads,
Those lofty ideals we hold so dear.
They drive our dreams away with our fear.
Are you living your dreams today?
Did everything you hoped for come your way?
Are you still waiting for that big opportunity,
That will fill your heart and soul for all eternity?
Never fear that you will not get your dreams,
It sometimes finds you quicker than it seems.
This life that you are living and also loving today,
Was created in your mind on a tranquil dreamy day.

What are you missing in your life today?

We often feel that we have something missing,
    That one thing we really want and need.
That simple little thing to make life complete,
That tiny part that would make life so sweet.
Some people miss a good friend to speak to,
Some miss going out to their favourite spots.
People miss their loved ones gone ahead,
They count the stars as they lie in bed.
A child misses going out to play,
On a cold and wet rainy day.
A dog misses his mistress or his master,
To take him out when the weather is clear.
A childless couple miss the children,
They wanted to have and never did.
A couple with children misses their time together,
As they watch a troublesome sister and brother.
What are you missing in your life today?
Could it be a friend, a place or something else?
Your life is the way it was planned to be,
Live, love and enjoy it, as it is your destiny.

The Sketchbook

Every day she did her sketches,
     It was her routine to practise daily.
She loved to draw people and so many other things,
Flower, birds, animals and butterflies with silver wings.
Jane loved to sketch and paint,
It brought her world to life.
She sat at her window every day,
Watching the world go by anyway.
She wished that she could move around,
To see the beauty of the city and town.
Doing her sketches made her happy,
She loved sketching every flower and tree.
Jane was bound to her wheelchair,
As a young child after she fell of her horse.
The sketchbook gave her freedom in her artistry,
Several sketches a day to record her life journey.

The Faces of Love

Where does love come from, I dare to ask?
  Does it originate in the heart and in the eyes?
Love is a powerful force that can change you,
It can make your heart soar to the blue skies.
There is a warmth that you feel inside,
A smile of love that you cannot hide.
There is a change in your mood, like a shift,
A feeling of love is like a happy gift.
She smiled whenever she looked at him,
He smiled whenever he looked into her eyes.
Their romance was a secret that they held silently inside,
In a world where hatred was first and love tossed aside.
Their love was a Sun that was radiant and pure,
They were always together in heart and in soul.
Their faces were lit with romantic fires in their eyes.
Love is always a joyful and passionate surprise.

Storm and Lightning in her Heart

There was a pain inside her chest,
    Her heart was beating so rapidly.
June knew that she had to have courage,
To go forward onto that sacred stage.
There was thunder and lightning,
Deep within her heart and soul.
She was worried and hoped it was good,
That this decision would make her whole.
He was a good man, this she knew well,
But people do change over time.
It was a lottery and it was a haze,
Falling in love was not a crime.
Should she marry the man she loved?
Was it the right decision, to marry so soon?
The night brings uneasiness and fear,
In her love, she shed a silent happy tear.
June was going to marry her beloved the next day.
They had overcome so much together, in every way.
The young bride and groom married the next day,
They are happily married, more than words can say.

Do you believe that an exchange of Ideas is useful?

There are some people who are scared,
Yes, they are scared to share their ideas.
What if the other person takes my ideas,
And makes them earn him or her millions?
These are some of the questions,
That go around in their heads,
They are sleepless, lying in their beds.
Ideas are everywhere,
They are in nature, in what we see,
They are in the air we breathe.
Ideas are sent from the universe,
To create articles, stories and verse.
Is that an idea that I hear and see,
Is it also a glimpse of creativity?
Do you believe that an exchange of ideas,
Is useful for everyone concerned?
Some people feel that meeting other writers,
To communicate and exchange ideas,
Is the best way to evolve and to grow.
The greatest writers had their writer friends,
When ideas were explored and so were trends.
Communication helps us all to learn and grow.

Exchanging a few ideas can also help,
To generate so many more.
Exchanging ideas and thoughts helps us,
To develop as writers and creators in the crafts.
Great stories told and great stories shared,
Are worth a barrel of gold and hearty laughs.

Waiting for Inspiration

He sat on his couch waiting for inspiration.
    He was sitting patiently waiting for an idea,
A few more minutes and he was in perspiration.
His mind was fuzzy and nothing was very clear.
She sat at her desk waiting to be inspired.
It was always difficult for her to get an idea.
Every thought she was receiving in her head,
She wrote down in her notepad in red.
Do you need to wait to get inspired?
Are you anxious when ideas do not seem to appear?
There are a million ideas waiting to be used,
A million more for you, so overcome your fear.
Inspiration comes out of the blue,
It can be an inspirational thought,
That is a gem of an idea waiting to grow.
Start writing it and you will get many more.

The one cup of Coffee she could not have

Rachel got up late that morning,
　　She was getting late for work.
Rachel needed one cup of warm coffee,
To make her feel alert and filled with energy.
She bought a cup as she got off the train.
It was a warm cup of great looking coffee.
She could not resist it; she was not strong willed.
She walked, she tripped and her coffee spilled.
Rachel had to make the next coffee at work.
She prepared a fresh cup of the drink,
To take into her first morning meeting,
A colleague dropped her cup as he was tweeting.
It seemed to Rachel that she was not getting that drink.
A friend made her a nice great cup of coffee at home.
As she was about to drink her steaming cup,
Her cat jumped and spilled it from her cup.
That day Rachel decided to forget her drink,
It seemed that something was always coming between,
Rachel and that refreshing cup of strong coffee.
That particular day Rachel was caffeine free.

Writing Prompt: How do you include stories into your conversations?

There are some people who can fascinate you with the stories that they weave into their daily conversations. I have known a few people like my dad and an ex-colleague who had the power to hold powerful conversations with the help of great stories.

There is a magnetic power in telling stories. The type of story being told should be relevant and it should fit into the conversation that is happening in the present. There are so many people who just scatter stories here, there and everywhere, with the hope that they can control the conversation and hold the attention of their audience. They do not succeed and lose their audience in a few minutes.

While there are some great conversationalists, who are also marvellous storytellers. These interesting individuals collect stories on a variety of subjects. They remember the stories they have collected, the essential points, which they adapt to different situations and for a number of conversations.

I try to remember stories to use in conversations. I do need a bit of practice, but like they say, practice makes perfect. Do you carefully place your short stories and anecdotes in your conversations or are you guilty of scattering them everywhere in your lectures and conversations?

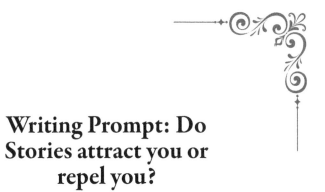

Writing Prompt: Do Stories attract you or repel you?

There are some individuals who enjoy listening and telling stories, while there are some people who do not like listening or telling stories. This could be because they did not grow up listening to stories or that stories were considered a waste of their time. Those people have lost a lot of stories indeed.

There are some individuals who love listening to stories and enjoy narrating stories whenever it is possible. I grew up listening to stories told to me by my parents. I heard the eastern and the western tales, as well as those created by my dad, who was a Master Storyteller.

I have sometimes heard people trying to tell a good story, but somehow it does not make an impact on the audience, as it was not delivered in a proper tone, or with the right expressions, by the storyteller. I feel that the way a storyteller tells his or her stories makes a big difference to the audience.

Do stories attract you or do they repel you and if so, why? Were you unfortunate enough not to grow up listening to stories or do you consider yourself fortunate, that you did not need to listen to stories? Do you love stories and who do you love them so much? Is it because it helped you as a child to allow your imagination to soar?

Writing Prompt: Inside the Box was.....something interesting

Have you ever had the experience of finding a box, an ordinary looking box, with no address label, no marking, as to what is inside the box? I have had the experience of locating a box at home and then trying to figure out exactly what is inside the box. It is really exciting, as I tried to guess its contents. I picked up the box, trying not to be too rough while handling it, just in case there were fragile items inside.

After five minutes of trying to imagine what the contents of the box could be, I finally opened the plain brown cardboard box, at my parent's home to find a treasure. It was a collection of photos taken out by my father from decades ago. It had old black and white photos, that were stuck and faded, photo negatives, that were stuck together. It was a pleasant surprise and the mystery of the unmarked box was solved.

Have you had similar experiences of finding boxes that were unmarked and then it is a guessing game to imagine what could be inside the box? Use this writing prompt to recall and record those moments when you found a mystery box and it was an exciting experience for you. Did you find a treasure, an heirloom or something utterly ridiculous in an unmarked mystery box?

The residential Rat

I t was an old house,
   It had planks falling off here are there.
There were cobwebs in hidden places,
There were rat droppings everywhere,
Even in the most unusual of spaces.
The children of the home,
Ran from room to room without a care.
There were not afraid of the roaches,
Or the rodents that lived in the walls.
It was an old house and Mold was everywhere.
The parents tried their best,
To keep the home clean at all times.
The children dropped their food on the ground,
Which the rodents ate when no one was around.
The cats moved stealthily without making a sound.
Would this rodent paradise ever end?
As he invited his family and every friend.
This was the kingdom of the residential rat,
He chews on the supplies and grows mighty fat.
He proudly proclaims that he also rode a cat.

In the Heat of the Moment

S ometimes when tempers flare,
  We can say things we do not mean.
In the heat of the moment a lot can be said,
A lot can be done that cannot be undone.
In the heat of the moment,
He called his friend a liar, it really stung.
He could not take those words back,
From that moment he controlled his tongue.
In the heat of the moment,
She threw his ring into the sea.
That one action split them apart,
She lost the love of her beating heart.
In the heat of the moment,
He fired his best worker and chef.
His restaurant closed down very soon,
He now sings a very different tune.
In the heat of the moment,
A lot can happen, we later regret.
Controlling your emotions and anger,
Is a life lesson no one should forget.

Writing Prompt: What if you had a different first name in Life?

I am quite comfortable with my name. Are you happy with your first name? I am a Warren, would I have been comfortable with a name like Henry, Larry or Gary? It is hard to say, but it is possible that my life would have been different in some ways. I would not have been Warren Brown, the Writer. Perhaps, I would have been Henry Brown, the Lawyer, or Larry Brown, the stage performer or Gary Brown, the extreme sports enthusiast.

Are you comfortable with your name and what are the names that you could have had and what are the types of persons you would have been? This is an exercise in finding the limitless possibilities that you can imagine. What are the sports or crafts that you like, that you could see yourself doing in life. Yet, as yourself today, you are doing something that you do not really enjoy, yet you harbour a dream of doing so much more in life.

The truth I have found is that you do not need to have a different name to have an interesting life. There are people who do a variety of jobs and have a wide range of interests and do what they truly enjoy without changing their names. They are the best version of themselves, while doing all that they truly love in life. Are you one of these people who do not need to change their names, in order to have a fuller and more satisfying life?

Time for a Reboot

What if every day, in the future, was a new day?
You are a new person at the start,
You have a new personality,
A new job that you love.
A new spouse and family, with a cup of tea.
A brand-new person for a new day,
To do everything you love every day.
Every night as you close your eyes,
Your brain gets a reboot, to a new you.
A new personality comes to you,
With a new life and social world.
The reboot is the life of future humans,
When we change our lives and our minds.
A machine we all have at home is plugged in,
To change who you are as a person from within.
Tomorrow is a brand-new day,
The person and life you have today,
Is erased and you are changed in every way.
Are you ready for the new reboot of your mind,
The next best invention since AI stepped in.
A better life you will never live or find.
Go home and get plugged in to the machine,
For an experience never lived or seen.

A World of Happy Heart Memories

There is a special place,
That we all know about but seldom visit.
There is a sacred place deep within our minds,
Where we hold our cherished memories.
It is a place where there is green grass,
A place where the skies are always blue.
Where our deepest wishes come true.
In this world of happy memories,
We find our loved ones who we have lost,
To this world and who we miss every day.
This world of peace is brimming with goodness,
That dwell as strong and joyful heart memories.
There is happiness and peace in this world,
Even the breeze is musical in the trees.
In this world of golden memories,
That we hold deep within our hearts,
We can find love and comfort always.
In the Cathedral and sacred place inside,
There is a world where darkness cannot hide.
Memories we can never forget or lose,
Are the ones we love and always choose.

The Heart of the News

It is called "The Heart of the News",
    It is filled with the latest local news,
National news and special interest news.
Every ordinary person could share their views.
A man wrote poetry and it was the news.
This fictional newspaper is very popular,
Created by Warren the Writer, its Founder.
Among everyone in every city around the world.
"The Heart of the News" was read by everyone,
Regardless of the climate, the weather or the Sun.
Everyone person is special in that paper.
Every ordinary person was the focus.
A simple man can tell his story,
A simple woman can have her glory.
A girl published her favourite recipes,
A dish of vegetables, cheese and peas.
"The Heart of the News" is for everyone,
Regardless of your rank or your station.
Publish your story with heart in the news today,
Be a newsmaker and shaker in every way.
You are the heart in the news story,
It is your time for fame and glory.

Action movie weekend

A ction movies for me are bliss,
   They are so filled with thrills,
Adventures and so many spills.
Punching, throbbing adrenaline fuelled action,
You feel fully energized and ready to win.
There is no time to sit in a corner,
Look at the wall or out of a window,
Watching life passing by in the day.
The weekend for me is a time to relax,
To forget the week that has been,
To get revitalized with a dose of action.
This Saturday night it was the Batman,
The new caped crusader in Gotham.
Filled with action from start to finish,
I was injected with a dose of power,
Fuelling my creativity every passing hour.
This Sunday it is action with the Justice League.
High stakes and great action moments on screen.
Who can ask for more action and thrills?
As superheroes battle to fight and win the day,
Boosting my imagination and creativity in every way.

To be remembered or to be forgotten

There are some who want to be remembered,
For generations of mortals who will come.
Some want to be forgotten as the years go by,
They just want their time here to fly.
The ones who want to be remembered,
Are the ones who strive to do much in life.
The ones who wish to be forgotten,
Are the ones who do wrong or nothing in life.
When people wish to leave a lasting legacy,
Their work stretches out to the ends of eternity.
There are those who do not care about legacies,
They do not mind as they squander their destinies.
Do you wish to be remembered,
Like an everlasting Sun or a silver Moon?
Do you really want to be forgotten in time,
Like a bottle of emptied scarlet red wine?

Poet's Note: Today, marks three months since my father passed away on the 25th June 2023. I miss my father and created a museum in his memory.

The Weather Man was Wrong

I t is raining once again,
  The roads are slippery and wet.
We were not prepared for this rain,
No one wanted their clothes to stain.
The weather man told us it was sunny,
The bees were not out collecting honey.
The sun is shining brightly today,
We are wearing our heavy jackets,
We got our umbrellas ready for the rain.
The weather man was wrong once again,
We got sunshine when we expected rain.
Some of us bother about the weather,
The weather irritates some of us too.
Does the weather and the climate dictate?
Your mood and emotions at every date?
The weather man could be wrong or right,
We need to adapt and get ready accordingly,
When we look at the stars and skies tonight.
The weather man was wrong,
He told us it would be a sunny day.
The weather man was wrong,
He told us it would rain, once again,
We were unprepared, what a pain?

If there are stars in the dark skies tonight,
It will be a sunny day tomorrow, it is right.

The Fortune teller was Wrong

S he had her fortune told at a fair,
    She left that table in great despair.
The fortune teller told her the fortune,
Nothing was positive till the end of June.
The fortune teller was so very wrong,
She was financially able and strong.
His fortune did not sound very good,
There were parts he never understood.
He was told that great things would happen.
Nothing great ever happened to him,
He would always fail and never win.
The fortune teller's predictions,
Were like a whole pot of mental floss,
All he got was loss and more loss.
Are you one of those people?
Who believe everything the fortune teller,
Looks into her crystal ball and sees?
You could be someone who believes it all,
You could be someone who trust nothing at all.
If the fortune teller is wrong or right,
Live your life your way and do what is right.

Walking in the Darkness

A few people can walk in the darkness,
    Without stumbling and falling down.
Most people walk in the darkness,
Unable to see what lies ahead of them.
Do you have the eyes of a cat,
Able to walk in the darkest night,
With your uncanny eyesight?
Walking in the darkness is not easy,
It can leave you a bit dazed and queasy.
Walking through the darkness is easy,
When your eyesight is so sharp and precise,
That every shadow stands out in the night,
As clear as if it was broad daylight.
Are you walking in the darkness,
Through this life right now?
There are times when we ignore,
So much that lies in front of us,
As we keep looking for something more.
When you walk in the darkness,
Do you stumble often and fall,
Over your feet and into a wall?

The Spirals of Power of Ammonites

I t is said that there is energy in fossils today.
The ammonites are said to possess that power.
These cephalopods existed 66 million years ago,
They are shelled spiral shaped fossils existing today.
The ammonites are symbols of psychic power,
Negative energies are believed to enter one way,
Turning into positive energy as they exit,
At the end of the spirals the other way.
Do these fossils actually possess such power?
The type to turn negative into positive energies,
It is really difficult to prove and positively say.
We do know that blind beliefs come into play.
Powerful fossils of ammonite power,
Make the negative energies that swirl.
All around our disturbed and unhappy world today,
Get transformed into positive power someday.

Seeds of Stories in the Fields of the Cosmos

We all speak about stories, we would love to write stories, but we need to find those stories. Where could we possibly find the stories that we want to write? Those stories are not hidden away like we think they are. No, stories are present everywhere, waiting to be collected and told by those storytellers who are willing to plant them and grow saplings into trees of stories. The seeds of stories are present in the fields of the cosmos.

Close your eyes and imagine that in the cosmos there are large areas filled with the seeds of stories. These seeds of stories waiting to be told, are like tiny sparkling stars. Now visualize in your mind's eye, every tiny seed containing a story that is waiting to be told. Collect these star seeds of story, and plant them into the fertile and rich soil of your subconscious mind. Do this exercise before going to bed. You need to tell yourself that you are planting the seeds of great stories, before you drift off to sleep.

The next morning, before getting out of bed, close your eyes and imagine that you are viewing the fertile fields of your subconscious mind, where you had planted the seeds of stories the night before. Visualize small green saplings growing out of the soil. Imagine taking a watering pot and watering the field with the long rows of saplings of stories. You need to tell yourself that you are watering the saplings of awesome stories. Write down the first few ideas that come into your mind.

That night, you will notice that the saplings have grown into small trees, getting stronger every time, as they are watered. The next day, as you view the trees of stories you have planted in your subconscious mind, they are taller and stronger. This exercise will help your imagination to expand and to start the process of creating and developing your own seeds of stories into plants and finally trees of stories. Write the first few story ideas or poetry ideas that come into your mind.

Every tree of story, that you have grown in the field of your subconscious will deliver a story to you. Now, take a notepad and sit and begin to write the thoughts and ideas that come into your mind. Remember that every idea no matter how simple or mundane, has the potential to develop into a great story, written by you the creator and storyteller.

How to decide on the best ideas for stories?

As writers we are all on the constant look out for seed ideas, that we can convert into stories, poems or articles. As a writer I know the feeling of looking for ideas. I have found that we need to use all our senses as we search for the seeds of stories, that are waiting to be planted into our imagination.

The soft feeling of satin as you run your finger on the fabric, will make your mind imagine something that you can make into a story. The satin cushions where the old man sat, could be gradually transformed into a short story. The feel of satin could remind you of the sleek fur of a panther, as it moves silently through the forests stalking its prey, as a new story begins.

The sound of children playing in the rain, could be transformed into a story about children going on a holiday to a tropical island paradise, with their parents. On this island they find that there are mythical creatures. Are these creatures real, mechanical or the figments of the overactive imagination of children?

The taste of coffee in the morning, could be the spark needed for a story of a coffee bean farmer, who stows away on a plane to New York. The farmer wanted to visit the factory, where he was sending the coffee beans. The adventure and experiences of the poor farmer could become a great short story or a novel, if it contains the powerful seed of story.

When the writer sees a bird with an injured wing, lying on the roadside, she could take it back home and nurse it to health as its broken wing begins to heal. This action of the writer, could result in the creation of an imaginative story about a carrier bird, that was sent with a message on its wing, from a person who was held captive in a barn. The writer finds the message, which was a cry for help and she decides to do something about it as the story continues.

How do you decide on the best seed ideas to use for your stories? Write down all the ideas that come into your mind, discarding nothing. Later go through the list of your ideas and concentrate on those ideas that spark your imagination. You will find that at that time there are one or two ideas that you seem to be attracted to in your quest for stories. The best ideas for you to develop into stories, are the ones that you are drawn to and that seem to take on a life of their own. You will feel the power of that story idea, compel you to write your story. Think about the idea, write it down, brainstorm the idea for a while and keep it away. When you return to the idea, you will find that your thoughts begin to flow, as your imagination and creativity work together to create a wonderful and powerful story, poem or article. All ideas are stories waiting to bloom in the forest of stories in your imagination.

Stories speak to the Storyteller

A story is just an idea,
    That floats like a breeze in the air.
A story is just like a will-o-the-wisp,
That appears and disappears.
That little flash of golden light,
Disappears into the dark night.
Can stories speak to a Storyteller?
Stories take on a life of their own.
An urgency is created in the mind,
And the heart of the Storyteller.
The story needs to be told right now,
The story needs to be woven,
With the finest yarn of silken thread,
The ones that adorn a princess's bed.
The imaginative storyteller,
Feels the power of a story,
As he or she begins to weave the tale.
There is no stopping a story,
That needs to be told.
There is no stopping a story,
Till every part of it is retold.
A story is like a lovely flower,
That needs to be shown to the world.

A story is like a wonderful painting,
That needs to be displayed for all the see.
The creative and imaginative storyteller,
Can feel the power and passion of a story,
As he or she releases it into the world.
The story sets alight the fires of imagination,
Like the first fires of our earthly creation.

Under the Right Conditions

C onditions always change in life.
      Some conditions are just great,
They can help one overcome strife.
Life is filled with changing days,
Some days are powered with high energy,
While other ones are lazy hazy days.
Under the right conditions,
Great things can happen,
A failure can turn into a win.
With the right conditions,
In place for tiny embryonic new seeds,
They can grow away from the weeds.
Under the right conditions,
A woman can rise to rule a country,
With her voice heard over land and sea.
Under the right conditions,
Humanity can be at peace and achieve,
Everything that we always believe.
Under the right conditions,
Great things can and do happen,
When we change a negative situation.

The Spirit of the Sycamore Tree

The Sycamore tree has been cut down,
  The Acer pseudoplatanus tree has fallen.
Cut down in a moment of madness and rage,
The iconic tree lies broken on its earthly stage.
The Sycamore tree stood at Hadrian's Wall,
In the gap, it stood, strong, bold and tall.
Robin Hood stood at the tree in a movie scene,
A powerful moment on the silver screen.
The cut stump stands now at the gap,
Remnants of the majestic Sycamore tree.
A part of English heritage is now destroyed,
That strong presence is now part of history.
The sycamore cut down at Hadrian's Wall,
Still stands majestic, awesome and tall,
In the hearts and minds of the hundreds of the public,
Who mourned at the tree, during the pandemic.
The Spirit of the Sycamore tree,
Will shine for all time at the gap in the wall.
Life, history and humanity may come and go,
As a new tree finds its roots, to once again grow.

In Touch with the Earth

The child picks up the sand in her hand,
    She throws a spade of it into a red bucket.
The farmer lifts a handful of soft moist soil,
Knowing that it is the right time for growing.
The earth on which we stand,
Is the same earth from which we have come.
The soil from which we have our crops grown,
Is the land that nourishes our bodies, blood and bone.
Are you in touch with the Earth?
Do you take time to walk on the land?
Barefooted on this land we call home.
The same earth on which we always roam.
The earth grounds us to this reality,
It is our origin, our future and our destiny.
Get in touch with the Earth today and every day,
Evolve in every human, physical and spiritual way.

Every Step We Take we are changing the World

Now, how could you and I possibly change,
    This world that we live in, with its fortune and wings?
We feel at times that our lives are so small,
That we barely matter in the great scheme of things.
There are moments when we feel,
That our work here does not make a difference.
The normal trudge to school and work is so dull,
Not as free as a flying eagle or a diving seagull.
Every step that we take does make a difference,
We are meeting people, while living out our lives.
We are making a small difference in our world,
From a letter written, a cake baked to a flag unfurled.
The world is changing us in very subtle ways,
As much as we change the world every day.
Every step taken creates a mini revolution,
In the heart and soul of human evolution.
This is our world to live, love, create and celebrate,
Enjoy every opportunity of life before it is too late.
In this world every precious living breath we take,
Opens a new dimension of life of which we partake.

Breathing
Encyclopaedias of Stories

There are encyclopaedias of stories,
  Walking with us and about us every day.
We do not realize that we are passing by,
These great storehouses of stories every day.
In life we meet so many people,
Everyone so very different and rare.
In life we come across so many lives,
Some that are beyond compare.
Everyone in life is a living library,
An encyclopaedia of stories so great.
Discover the stories of people you know,
Do it today, before it is too late.
Everyone is an encyclopaedia of stories,
With stories, fables and tales, from A to Z.
These living breathing libraries of stories,
Are as beautiful as majestic flowering trees.
Share your encyclopaedia of stories,
For a world of writers and readers to enjoy.
This is your opportunity to uncover and discover,
Tales of failures, triumphs, successes and joy.

How is it in Heaven?

M um and Dad, does it rain in heaven,
　　　Or is it always sunny and bright?
I wonder if there is always daylight,
With no sign of darkness and night.
Dearest Dad and Mum in Heaven,
I think of you both a lot it is true.
I know that you are both happy together,
Living in peace, in love, with joy, forever.
Perhaps it does not rain in heaven,
Like it does here in our troubled world.
There are no tears to be shed in Heaven,
Like there are so many tears in our world.
There may not be lightning and thunder,
In that world beyond the stars called Heaven.
Do birds fly in that world of peace, like Angels do?
The power my love keeps me close to both of you.
*Poet's Note: A poem in memory of my mother Joan and my father,
Melvyn who passed away three months ago, 25 June 2023.*

A Letter from a Father to His Son

Good morning, Warren,

You must miss me a lot. I miss all those conversations that we would have. Thank you so much for always being there for me, although we lived miles, continents and oceans apart. I knew that you loved me and still do.

Remember Son, that your mother and I are always here for you. Whenever, you need us just ask and we will guide you in whatever you do in life. Thank you for taking care of the home, my work and my legacy.

As a writer you have miles to go with your writing work. Always remember to keep writing as that is your strength and your passion. You have been writing since you were a teenager. I also started writing when I was in my teens and continued contributing my work to a magazine till my last earthly days. The path of a writer is not easy, but it is rewarding, as the seeds of ideas we sow, can make the world a better place. I always enjoyed planting seeds in my writings, knowing that it would inspire others for years and generations to come.

Nothing is permanent in life and that we need to do all the good that we can in this life as there are riches in heaven for us. There are mansions in Heaven and in those mansions, there are homes for each and every one of us. Do not worry about your mother and myself. We are happy now that we are together after being apart for fifteen years.

Thank you for taking me to your home and for showing me all the things that you do and enjoy so much, like watching movies, cooking, writing, shopping and taking care of the home and family. I wish that I could have visited you once again, But, do not worry, we are here for you and your wife at all times.

Always try to do as much good as you can in this life, as this helps to accumulate blessings for you in Heaven. Try to be kind, tolerant and understanding the people, as we are all just human and we all have our faults. This is not always easy, but it is possible.

Money is not the most important thing in life. Money is not everything. The good that you do matters more and God works in mysterious ways his wonders to perform. Everything happens for a reason and we are just the instruments that God uses to do his work on Earth.

The spiritual plane is not a scary place and the power of prayer should not be underestimated. The soul is very real and it is more powerful than our physical bodies and continues to exist in the spiritual realm. Our birth and death is not the beginning and end of our lives, our work continues in the next dimension.

I knew that the day would come when I would have to tell you Goodbye. Parents are not immortal and we do not live forever, we are always by your side. It was not a final goodbye, as we will meet again. We will all be together once again as a family. Life continues and life is for living, so follow your dreams.

God Bless You Son
Your Mother and I Love You
Now and Forever
Dad

Writer's Note: My father Melvyn Brown, was taken away on the 25th of June 2023. It is now four months since my dad passed away in Kolkata, India. This letter was written today, the 28th of October, by me. It is an imaginary letter I wrote from my dad to me, as I could hear his voice in my mind, like a conversation we would have over the phone almost every day of the week, before he left this earthly plane.

Creating Futures- What future will you create today?

We always talk about the future, and we look forward to it. Sometimes we try to plan for the future, we lay out a set of plans about what we want and what we plan to do. The future is hazy, and we try to visualize it as best as we can.

The future has several outcomes. It is up to us to make choices. Every choice that we make opens a different future. Suppose we could create several futures every day. Is it possible to create many futures? Yes, we can create ten or a hundred possible futures, in our minds with the power of imagination. However, we can only live one future.

The desire that impels us to action is the one that holds our attention. Therefore, the future that we want is the one that we infuse with desire. We are always working towards the future we want and we know that it will materialize for us.

If you create two different futures today, which one would you choose? If I could create three or four or five different futures, I would choose the one that I desire, the one which will help me to grow and evolve as an individual. I will choose the future that gives me everything I need and desire in life.

Try creating different futures today in your imagination. Visualize yourself living the different futures in your mind. Watch as you live the different futures. Now choose the future that you want to live. Choose the future that will make you happy and fulfilled as an individual. You have the power to create your own future using the power of your mind and imagination.

Foot soldiers in the march of life

E very morning the march of life begins.
   Getting up and going in to work.
Working at our jobs to pay the bills.
We are the good foot soldiers in life,
Living, loving, working, through joy and strife.
We are the remarkable foot soldiers of life.
Every evening as the sun begins to set,
While the birds fly in the twilight,
The good foot soldiers make their way home.
They walk and travel in trains and automobiles.
They are all eager to rest as they reach home.
To enjoy that moment of bliss and peace,
With their loved ones so full of cheer,
As they eat dinner and drink cool beer.
If every evening was an art piece,
It would be as colourful as Jason's fleece.
We are the good foot soldiers in the march,
Always in a hurry to be somewhere,
Always in a rush to get the day done,
We are the hardworking foot soldiers,
Completing our tasks here on earth,
Starting at the time of our birth.
We are all given a mission to fulfil,

To contribute our efforts in the world.
We are the foot soldiers on these paved streets,
Drumming our shoes on these paths.
We are the foot soldiers walking in eternity,
Waiting to finally rest in joy and serenity.
We are the foot soldiers walking towards home,
The day is finally done, there is nowhere to roam.

All the roads of life Take us back home

As we walk on the roads of life,
We discover so many things about ourselves.
As we walk on this ever-changing journey,
We experience so many different emotions,
We love, we play, we hurt and we live.
All the roads of life,
Take us back home to where we want to be.
All the roads of life,
Help us to understand the enigma of our destiny.
No matter where we go and what we do,
The roads of life lead back to the real You.
You begin your journey on the road of life,
You go out into the world to discover,
The true meaning of your life and destiny.
You walk on the roads of life,
There are so many paths and crossroads,
Everyone looks more enchanting than the other,
We take on roles of son, father, sister, mother, and brother.
On this never-ending journey, we increase our loads,
We struggle to comprehend life's puzzling codes.
The further we walk, the longer the path seems to be,
Discarding our burdens will help reveal our destiny.
All the roads that we walk in life,

On the well-trodden path, under the sky so blue,
Will lead you back to the new and evolved You.
We are the travellers on our long journey,
Never knowing what to expect in life.
The struggles make us stronger,
It gives us the spiritual power to overcome strife.
We continue traveling and move one step further,
To discover who we can and will eventually be,
The grand revelation of our human destiny.
All the roads of life,
Take us back home to where we want to be.
All the roads of life,
Help us to understand the enigma of our destiny.

Let the lamplighter walk down your dark street

E very evening the lamps are lit.
    The lamplighter walks on the streets,
He lights every lamp on the road of life.
The lamplighter in life are those little thoughts,
Those tiny little thoughts of wisdom that you gain,
That warm your heart and protect you in the rain.
The light of those street lamps in your life,
Fill your mind with inspiration and motivation.
Those tiny thoughts and concepts light a fire,
That helps you to bring life to your creation.
If you are a poet, artist, or writer of any type,
You will recognize the birth of an idea.
It is like a lamp of light has been switched on,
The idea keeps growing till it is fully born.
Watch the lamplighter in your life,
Illuminate your mind with ideas and creativity,
Those thoughts will burn through eternity.
Fill your life with more light and illumination,
With wondrous thoughts of creative imagination.
As you gaze at the road of your life,
In the glow of a hundred lamp-lights,
You will realize that we are like fireflies,
Our spirits can light up the dark skies,

Our thoughts are like burning fireflies.
The lamplighter of Creation has gifted the fire,
To take our minds and spirits so much higher.
Let the lamplighter walk down your dark street,
As the fires warm the cold air with heat.
Lighting every lamp as they pass every door,
The light of knowledge burns with a warm glow.
Watch them move with soundless feet,
Silent movements with a harmonious beat.
Spreading the light of illumination everywhere,
Like creativity and imagination in the night air.

Travel with me to Infinity

The skies are never ending,
    The galaxies are spread across space.
The universe is never ending,
The cosmos moves in every place.
Come let us sail into infinity,
Let us travel in this large vessel,
That sails on the sea of endless time,
From here to the celestial clime.
There is not end in sight,
There are moments of darkness,
There are moments of sadness,
There are moments of light.
Our ship keeps sailing in infinity,
There is no end in our sight.
Moving ahead is our destiny.
We pass worlds much like ours,
We pass ancient planets,
With strange looking plants and flowers.
We sail slowly and drift in space,
In orbits and circles we sail and go.
There is no ending and no beginning,
There is only time endlessly flowing.
Come sail with me to infinity,
That is our purpose and destiny.

Poet's Note: This is my 2001st literary piece on Medium and it is appropriate that the subject of this poem is about Infinity, that has no end. Imagination and creativity are like the circle, there are no sides, there are no angles, it just goes on never ending and never beginning.

The writer can keep creating for as long as his or her human life allows, till he leaves the material plane to end the vast infinite spiritual plane, where existence, imagination and creativity move ahead into infinity.

It all starts with Imagination

When you look at the light bulb, you wonder how it was created. When you look at a rocket going into space you wonder how it came to be created. When you see a movie, you think about how it was created. Everything that is in our present reality was first a fantasy in the creator's mind. Edison visualized an object that could radiate electricity, to give us light. It was this fantasy that he later designed to become the electric bulb.

A movie was first an idea, then a rough script and finally a completed written script, submitted to a movie producer by the scriptwriter. All ideas that eventually become physical creations all start in the imagination of its creator.

An architect builds a structure, either a building or a bridge, based on an image he has created in his mind. He later puts that design into a two-dimensional sketch to a complete blueprint of the structure. It is the same imagination and creativity of the architect, that becomes a complete structure built of concrete, sand, stones, and metal.

Our imagination slowly creates our reality. If we want to change our reality, we need to use the power of our fertile imagination to make changes. Use the power of your imagination to write your stories and poems, to change your life, to fill it with positivity. The power of our minds are unfathomable, we just need to believe, that whatever we visualize in our minds, we can create in the real world.

Jumping Over Hurdles

The journey has begun and we are all part of the race of life. In this race there are a number of hurdles on an obstacle course. Every hurdle needs to be leaped over if we are going to win this race. In this competition we have many competitors, who are all taking part in this obstacle course called life.

You jump over the first hurdle, then run a little further and leap over the second ,the third hurdle. The more obstacles we leap over the harder the race seems to become for its competitors. As we approach the middle of the race, we are now jumping over the hurdles mechanically. We have forgotten the reasons for taking part in this race.

An hour has passed. There are just five more hurdles left for us to jump over. We now remember the reason we are taking part in this race. We have a destination in mind. We are going to rest at the end of this race. However, we need to be focussed on the present, the here and now.

The runners are all running at high speed on the racetracks. They are now giving the race that last burst of energy as they jump over the hurdles and the final lap is just a few minutes away. There are several runners who had begun the race with great zeal but stopped and dropped out of the race.

The runners are now fully focussed on the race ahead. They can visualize the end as they keep running. The winner runs past the ribbon at the end of the race. She gets the first place in the race, as the second and the third runners run over the finishing line.

What motivates you in life as a runner and jumper as you take part in this race of life? Is it the promise and the hope of what lies ahead or is it the smell of the reward and the fulfilment of your ambitions? In this world of life's hurdles and obstacles, I keep focussed on the purpose of my life and that motivates me to keep writing and sharing my ideas with the world.

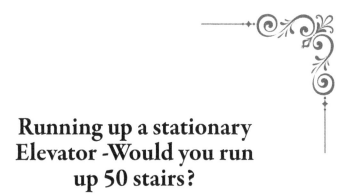

Running up a stationary Elevator -Would you run up 50 stairs?

The second elevator going up at the tube station has stopped working. Would you run up 50 stairs to get to the top or would you walk up the stairway? Running up those fifty stairs would be faster especially if there is a crowd of a hundred waiting to go up to the top level to leave the station. It is the office rush, and most commuters are later as they go to work, with train delays.

Walking up the stairs would take some time, with fifty people in front of you and another fifty behind you. If you run up the stairs, you will feel exhausted by the time you reach the top. If you walk up the stairs or use the second elevator you will not be tired.

You could either walk up the stationary elevator, run up the stationary elevator or go up the second working elevator, with a number of commuters standing. What would you do, if it is rush hour and you have five minutes to reach work?

If I was given the same situation with the same options, I would run up the stationary elevator stairs. I would do this to simply prove to myself, that it can be done, and it would save me time. Perhaps, it is also a statement to myself that nothing can slow me down in life. Whatever the situation or obstacle in life, it can be overcome. Every decision we make in life, shapes our mind and our life.

Perhaps, it is also a way to demonstrate the fact that it is possible to run up fifty steps with a focussed mind. This is one way to ensure that the mind and the body are working in perfect harmony. It is better to say, "in harmony", as nothing can be perfect in life, as we are all humans and humans are not perfect beings. This was a motivating moment for me today as I ran up fifty stationary elevator stairs, staying focussed on my goal of completing the run without faltering once. It can be done, and it is possible.

Flight of the Falcon

With precision and speed,
    The falcon swoops,
To get its elusive prey.
The flight of the falcon,
Will help you to aspire,
With unbridled ambition,
To the heights of freedom,
To the triumphal clarion of victory,
As the falcon flies from the tree.

The Race of the Cheetah

The cheetah is on the brink,
    The very edge of extinction.
Like a cheetah we need to be fast,
As swift as the speed of light.
We need to evolve, adapt in life,
Or face extinction over time.
Meditate within the hour,
To find your racing cheetah.

The Bear of Comfort and Protection

The strength and confidence,
   Of the bear will see you,
Through difficult times.
Like the bear of courage and determination,
You will achieve the impossible.
Patience and playfulness,
Will carry you in life.
As you meditate and ask to win,
You will be comforted and embraced,
By the strong bear of protection.

The Writer's Edge

Almost every writer I know, including myself is sometimes hesitant when writing and publishing a piece of work. We are not sure if the story, poem, or article will be liked by our readers. Perhaps the piece needed to be rewritten, edited, and re-read before it was published. This is possible, when you have a small group of readers who read your work before you publish it, and it could be your friends or family members. However, if you want to read and publish your work immediately, then it is up to you to read, review and publish your work.

For a writer to have an edge he or she needs to create something that is unique and has his or her particular creative style, in its creation. Confidence is a key factor in enabling a writer to keep creating work which is what his or her readers want. When a writer is confident in his or her ideas and knows the value of them, he or she can create the most amazing literary pieces, which are enjoyed and shared by readers.

A writer can only move ahead fearlessly in the literary world, when he or she collects ideas and converts them into stories, articles, or poems. These created stories need to be published as soon as possible, as well as shared on social media platforms. Readers are always on the look out for new content to read. Search engines like google are regularly searching for fresh content, to list on their websites, so that readers who search with keywords can find the latest content related to that topic online.

When a writer hones his or her craft, he or she evolves into a better writer over time. Almost every writer, is a work in progress. He or she is constantly looking for the right words, ideas, and ways to present a story, for maximum impact on the mind of the readers. Be confident in your abilities as a writer and surge ahead fearlessly, into the literary world.

Keep Your Eyes Open

The universe unfolds its tapestry,
  Every day it opens a new possibility.
The magic of creation is serenity,
Unfolding across the cosmic sea.
Open your eyes and you will see,
The magic and the mystery.
The universe speaks in common ways,
Simple actions in nights and days.
Open your eyes and you will dream,
A world of possibilities unseen.
Living your life is not a crime,
Enjoy the rain, sunshine and grime.
Be cheerful and try to grin,
You can and you will win.
The cosmic force is ever flowing,
It is always observing and so knowing.
Walk towards your cosmic vision,
Changing your life is your decision.
Train your eyes and your mind,
To live a life less unkind.
You are the thread of creation,
Hold your head high and breathe in.
You can cross the barriers of time,
A mountain that you can climb.

Keep your eyes and mind open,
You will always, always, always win.

Fascination with Music
and Melodies

"*E*verything in the universe has a rhythm, everything dances.*"
Maya Angelou

Music has the power to help a person to feel better and to improve their mood. I have always been fascinated with the power of music and song to make a difference in the lives of individuals. Music therapy is the method by which a trained professional helps to alleviate the mental state of a person.

Music does help in reducing stress and brings about positive changes for a person, while also treating depression. You must be familiar of the effect that music has on your mood and mental state of mind. When you are feeling under-the-weather and happen to hear an upbeat song on the radio or on your iPod, your mood immediately changes.

Music can draw us into the words and melodies of a song. A sad song will evoke sad memories while a song about the joys of love and romance will put you into a romantic mood. A familiar song can transport you back in time to a special moment in your life. The power of music is used to create positive changes in the mind and life of an individual through music therapy.

You do not need to be a music therapist to use the power of music to improve your mind and your life. You could start by doing the following as part of your personal mood enhancement method in music therapy:

1. List and listen to your favourite songs.
2. Keep a list of songs to make you happy when you feel sad.
3. Make a list of songs to improve your mind when you are stressed.
4. Have a list of songs to motivate you when you feel de-motivated.
5. Write your own songs when you are feeling lonely, sad, depressed and when you are feeling positive.
6. Sing your favourite songs, that can be both uplifting and inspirational.
7. Dance by yourself or with a partner to your favourite songs.
8. Keep a music journal of your best songs and why you love them.
9. Write an article about how music has helped you to change your life and mood.
10. Record your own songs, upload them to YouTube and share them for the world to enjoy.

Spread the word about the power of music and you will be making a positive change in the world, one melody at a time.

Fascination with Photographs

"Photography is the story I fail to put into words."
     – Destin Sparks

I was looking through several photo albums last week and they brought back so many memories from the time I was a child and a teenager. These were warm and happy emotions and they lit my heart with happiness. Photographs have a way of taking you back into time to those special moments when you were with loved ones, who have passed away. This is an uplifting walk down memory lane.

I have always been fascinated with photography and the power of photographs to make you feel more inspired, motivated and happier in life. Whatever we do, hear and see does make an impact in your life. When you feel happy looking at photographs of yourself from the past, your brain registers it as a happy memory and similar memories flood into your mind.

Photography has evolved over the years. There are still individuals who use the best made cameras to get the best photographs of animals, plants, people and places. However, photography is not limited to cameras anymore. You can now capture your golden moments with friends and family, with the help of your mobile phone. There is no film roll that needs to be put into our camera, in the day of digital photography.

Photo albums will become antiquated in the age of digital photography. However, printed photos are still a marvel and feel wonderful to hold in your hands, whether they are printed on matte or on glossy paper. Professional photography has not disappeared and still has a place in the future, as the field of photography has also advanced and evolved over time.

There are times in life when we forget to take out photographs and realize that we missed capturing special moments. Whether you are an amateur or a professional photographer, keep photographing your life and all those people, places and things that matter to you. This pictorial journal will be a treasure trove of memories because a picture is definitely worth a thousand words.

Fascination with Food

That vital component of life that makes living beings, plants and animals enjoy this life on Earth, is food. The fruits, vegetables, meats, poultry, and all that we consume gives us the energy to fulfil our destiny.

I have always been fascinated with food, from childhood. I would get up in the morning and look forward to the delicious meals Mum would prepare. My mother was a great chef, and she would prepare culinary wonders for the family, relatives and friends. My mum introduced me to shopping for fresh meat and vegetables. I still look forward to shopping for groceries every week.

I have always been an observer of life. My dad always told me that observation is the key to understanding life. As a child I was more interested in eating tasty food. As a teenager I was curious to see how Mum would prepare her food. As an adult Mum told me to pay closer attention to her cooking methods, as it would help me later in life.

Today, I enjoy cooking dishes as much as I enjoy shopping for fruits, vegetables, and meats, as my wife and I put them all together to prepare dishes to eat and relish. Cooking is like science, where a lot of materials are put together, with spices and placed on a fire to combine them into a delicious preparation. There are materials, a recipe, a method, and an end product when the process is completed.

It is always important to pay attention and appreciate the food we eat in life, as it will then have a positive effect on your bodies. There are some people who consume food, without paying attention to what they are eating and so it is not properly digested by their bodies.

I like visualizing food as energy blocks that we consume, which in turn is absorbed by our bodies to release the energy we need to fulfil over everyday activities in the world. Appreciate the food that you eat and watch the way your life is transformed from the way you think to the way you view the world and work.

Get Started on your Memoir

We have so many interesting stories to tell in life. These stories are the life experiences we have had over the years, which include our observations on the world, as well as our reactions to the occurrences in life.

Every individual on the planet has a vast number of memories which are unique and special to that person. I am sure that you have so many memorable incidences in your life, that you would love to tell the world about. You can do that in your memoir, which would be a collection of your life stories.

If you do plan to start writing a memoir of your life or the life of someone else, like a family member, keep these points in mind:

1. Have a starting point, it could be from the present going back into the past or from the past leading to the present.
2. Make a list of all the stories that you can remember in a brainstorming session.
3. Develop each life story into a complete chapter.
4. Include all the characters in as much detail as possible in your stories.
5. Remember to add the years and the dates for your stories.
6. Describe the setting in which the story takes place.
7. Were there any memorable world events that took place during the time of your story?

8. Give your story an exciting start, give the story an interesting middle and a great climax.

9. Add suspense and tension to all your stories, so that it becomes a page-turner.

10. Your perspective and how you evolved as a person is vital to make your memoir a bestseller and one that will entertain readers.

11. "A picture speaks a thousand words", so try to include illustrations and photographs to your stories.

12. If you are the principal character of the memoir add impact to your stories by adding your views and what you did in every story.

13. All characters have their flaws and their weaknesses so make it a point to bring them to the attention of your reader.

14. Every story is a learning experience for us. Highlight the lesson learned at the end of every story in your memoir.

15. You can publish your memoir independently or send it to a publisher.

I look forward to reading your memoir soon. I feel in my humble opinion that my writings are a type of memoir of who I am as a person, as it reflects the way I feel, think, act and live. Get started on your memoir today and make it a bestseller on the Amazon Bestseller List.

The Zebra Crossing

The lights have changed,
The pedestrians can walk across,
The long and empty Zebra crossing.
The rush across the white lines,
Increases more than ten times.
The children holding hands,
Rush across as mother pulls them,
They need to cross the finish line.
The woman with the baby,
Pushes the pram across the crossing,
The blind man is pulled across,
By the friend who is in a hurry.
There is a rush, a run and a scurry,
As everyone wants to make it across.
The elderly couple look very cross,
As the lights have changed,
They could not walk across.
The rush across the zebra crossing,
Is a comical sight to behold,
Not for the nervous, but for the bold.
The crossing is so necessary and good,
In every city and neighbourhood.
Yet, there are cars that still zip across,
Just when pedestrians walk across.

If you are a driver of a vehicle,
You need to stop when lights change,
So that pedestrians can rush across in peace,
Giving their lives a longer lease.
The lights have changed,
The cars have stopped again.
The pedestrians race across once again.
The elderly couple slowly rush,
They are upset, it is all too much.
The three children skip across those lines,
Hopping and skipping in record time.
The man carrying a heavy sack,
Rushes like he is on a racetrack.
The funniest rush always starts,
Across the zebra line crossing,
With people rushing,
While children hop and sing.
The lights have changed once again,
The zebra crossing is empty once again.
The cars thunder across those white lines,
Till they rest at the next stop sign.

The Hungry for Knowledge Tourist

S he looked at the old parchments,
  So fragile, brittle and so very rare,
It was the beginning of her love affair.
Studying every inch of the document,
She knew what every sign and symbol meant.
It was an old piece from the museum,
So delicate and so precious a medium.
Searching for knowledge was her game,
Doing anything else was just too lame.
Judy visited the libraries around the world,
Researching into subjects ancient and rare.
She studied and visited the great universities,
Finding solutions to life's unsolved mysteries.
Searching for secret knowledge was her goal,
Knowledge investigation was her chosen role.
Judy was a knowledge tourist of repute,
Discovering greats leads on every route.
She visited libraries and monasteries worldwide,
Making friends and meeting professors on every side.
The keys to knowledge and wisdom she found,
In hidden places on and below ground.
Knowledge tourism was her soul purpose,
Her enthusiasm you could never miss.

If you have a hunger for ancient wisdom,
You know that you will find freedom,
If you choose to be a knowledge tourist,
The wisdom keys are on your checklist.

The Candle in the Window

The wick is lit when the day is born,
The light is over when the day is gone.
The flame of the candle burns bright,
Through the day and through the night.
The road is lit for us to follow,
Under the light of the candle glow.
There is always a light in the window,
It helps us to evolve and to grow.
The candle in the window gives its light,
That helps life to shine so bright.
We are each like a candle in life's window,
We discover who we are as we grow.
There is a light we follow every day,
That encourages us to grow in every way.
Our inner spirit is that candle flame,
It brightens our life every night and day.
The candle is the lighthouse on life's coast,
Guiding us to the life, we need the most.
The candle grows stronger and sends its light,
Guiding those lost souls through day and night.
Light the candle of enthusiasm in your life,
It will take you to happiness and out of strife.
Respect the candlelight that burns in everyone,

Every individual is a star, a moon and a sun.
We are all candles in the cosmic universe,
Moving through time and space we traverse.
Keep the candle of life burning so bright,
Through your earthly days and every night.

Jacob's Silver Tablets

The elderly man sat at his window,
  Looking down at his garden,
It looked so green after the rain,
It had come alive once again.
He saw something shining bright,
Under the silvery moonlight.
Jacob walked down to investigate,
He wanted to know what lay buried,
Just outside his garden gate.
There was something shining,
Buried in the mud and in the grass,
It was reflecting the light of the moon,
It looked like a large piece of glass.
Jacob was now very curious,
He really wanted to know,
This could be something or nothing serious.
He brought a large spade to dig.
He dug into the grass and the mud,
There were three large silver tablets,
All had strange inscriptions engraved.
He wiped the tablets as they shone,
In the light of the large full moon.
Did those silver plates have special powers?
Alien magic from beyond the stars.

Three nights later he had a dream,
In it he visited lands unusual,
With alien beings he had never before seen.
The next day things began to happen,
Jacob felt very different, he felt fresh and new.
The next-door neighbours were pleased,
To see a young man mowing the lawn.
They all thought that Jacob had no family,
Except his pet dog he buried under the apple tree.
The young man looked so much like Jacob,
He must be a nephew they all said.
Jacob moved to a new town and home,
The people were all too curious.
They wondered where Jacob had gone,
He told them that Jacob had died,
He was his long-lost son, called John.
The truth was that Jacob,
The old man of eighty-three,
Had become a young man again,
Barely over the age of twenty-three.
Those silver tablets and alien script,
Had transformed Jacob into a young man,
Perhaps, it was part of their mysterious plan.
There was no more old age with aches and pain,
Jacob was pleased to have his youth back again.
Did those silver plates have special powers?
Alien magic from beyond the cosmic stars.

What Lies Over the Hill?

What lies behind the closed door, what is in the closed box, what lies over the hill? These are just a few of the intriguing questions most of us ask ourselves, due to our natural curiosity, whether we are writers or not.

As a child I have always been curious about how things work, from the radio, the record player, to a movie projector. I wanted to know how things work, from the disc that plays music and sounds, to the radio transmitter and receiver, to the projector that displays images on a movie screen or a blank wall. Later in life I was curious to know how a computer works, to how does a website and a blog work. What are the skills needed to know that go into writing poems, stories and articles? These are just a few of the things that heightened my curiosity over the years.

Like most people I am an observer continuously on the lookout for a good story idea. When I see a hill, I wonder to myself, what could lie over that hill? If I was writing an environmental piece, a landfill could be on the other side of the hill. If I was writing a science fiction story, a secret structure could be over the hill or even a space craft with extra-terrestrials. The possibilities are endless when an individual is a creative writer. We can transform a simple environment or idea into a fascinating story. However, the writer needs to be enthusiastic about an idea and will then be able to create a story, poem or article that resonates with that same enthusiasm, because of that initial curiosity.

How curious are you as a creator and writer and do you imagine the possibilities that could exist? If you happen to be a creative writer, you will be comfortable with allowing your imagination to run wild and create something unbelievable. A curious writer can find a story everywhere. What lies over that hill, a new world, or a landfill?

Creating Magic in the Kitchen

S ue Ellen had big cooking plans,
　　As she arranged her pots and pans.
She needed to get her menu right,
With all the vegetables and meat in sight.
Today was a big day for her family,
It was her son's 21st birthday party.
Sue Ellen needed to get everything right,
From the roast to the ice cream delight.
All the relatives and friends were coming,
Including cousin Rachel who thought she could sing.
No one was looking to lovely Rachel's solo,
Including Uncle Jim who would always snore.
Harry was going to be twenty-one,
He was her beloved an eldest son.
Sue Ellen was busy in her large kitchen,
As the guests arrived, all storming in.
The most delicious food she was preparing,
The fried rice was cooking, and the soup needed stirring.
In a bowl were the roasted brown succulent potatoes,
As the aroma of food seductively wafted up every nose.
The fried sausages, mash potatoes, turkey and peas,
Looked as delicious as the hog roast and "jhaal frazee".
Sue Ellen and her husband Dan were beaming and proud,

As the family photos were taken with the large crowd,
While the energetic music played so loud.
Harry was going to be a famous physician,
While her son Gerry was going to be a musician.
Sue Ellen was the greatest chef and a magician,
With the delicious food magically made in her kitchen.

Photographs of Fairies

The two little girls believed in fairies.
        They imagined seeing them in the garden,
The imagined seeing them on the flowers.
The two young cousins saw flying fairies everywhere,
On the leaves, in the trees, and in the air.
Everything is possible in a child's imagination.
The world is filled with fantasy creatures.
Anything is possible in a creative mind,
Children see goblins and fairies of every kind.
The two cousins, Elsie and Frances photographed,
Those dainty fairies flying on wings,
With gnomes and other magical things.
Using the magic of clever photography,
The cousins fooled the world with the illusion,
Making the world believe in fairies was a delusion.
Thanks to their vivid and creative imagination,
The Cottingley fairies came to life,
Puzzling the experts far and wide,
As they watched fairies swim and glide.
Decades later, it was discovered that it was a hoax,
The fairies were just pictures cut-out,
Made to move like angels in the breeze,
Through the grass and the green leaves.
It was all just a childish playful joke.

In the mind of a playful child,
Nature and its mysteries come alive.
Let your imagination go free and wild,
Experience the world of a creative child.
https://www.historic-uk.com/CultureUK/The-Fairies-of-Cottingley/

The Pearl on the sand

The oyster grows the pearl,
In its shell at the bottom of the sea.
The waters moved around the shell,
As the speck grows in size,
In the shell where it lies.
The large pearl bursts,
Out of the tiny shell,
To roll out onto the shifting sand,
Where it lies in the waters,
At the bottom of the sea.
The pearl is finally free.
A large fish sees the pearl,
It swallows it whole.
A day later the fish is hooked,
It is chopped up and cooked.
The fish is placed on a dish,
As it is served for dinner.
However, the man nibbles it,
And discards the fish,
For a dish of chicken roast,
With a slice of brown toast.
The uneaten fish is taken,
Thrown into the kitchen bin.
There is heavy rain and strong winds,

A homeless man looks for shelter,
Away from the wild weather.
The tramp opens the bin,
He is elated to find the fish.
He devours it with relish,
He is astonished to find the pearl,
Nestled in the body of the fried fish.
The man is a tramp no more,
He is a millionaire who makes money grow.
He keeps the large pearl in a fish tank,
Watching is roll in the shifting sand.
That pearl in the sand changed his destiny,
He enjoyed his newfound prosperity.

The Earth on which we walk

We walk all our lives.
    We move here and there.
Living our lives as best as we can,
We end our days with a silent prayer.
We do our daily work,
We learn to walk and to run.
We spend our lives,
On this rock, under the morning Sun.
This planetary world that we call home,
Gives us so much to live and do.
We spend our years learning and growing.
We live our lives aware and knowing.
We are the living and breathing souls
Of this planetary rock that we call home.
You do not have to be a prophet or a seer,
To realize that we all have a purpose here.
We are the children of this rock we call home.
On this rock we live, love and roam.
We have made our lives on this rock.
We have built civilizations over the centuries.
We humans are as enduring as the rocks and trees.
We were born to love and to lovingly create,
Cities, Empires, and food on our plate.

Are we the minds of this world we call home?
Is the Earth speaking through us and all that we do?
Perhaps, we are the eternal souls of this living earth,
That has nourished us, our sweet Mother Earth.

Developing Creator Vision

I was just watching a video on Twitch.tv with Jim Lee doing a sketch of Spawn, the comic book character. A superhero trapped between two worlds, the world of the living and the world beyond. Jim Lee has his own unique artistic style; he begins by doing a rough sketch with a number of lines, that appear to be random, but are the basic shape of the figure. All is not as random as it appears to be on first looking at the sketch.

The second step is when Jim starts to highlight part of his rough sketch. It is only at this step, when he begins to ink the eyes, the outline of the figure that we begin to see the character emerge, like an angel being released from a block of concrete, like a Michelangelo sculpture. From this moment onwards Jim continues his inking, shading, and hatching, until the work is complete. Jim Lee is the celebrated Korean American artist and is currently the publisher and the Chief Creative Officer of DC comics. If you want to study comic book illustration, see the videos done by Jim Lee on You Tube.

When I write an article, story or poem, I keep writing my ideas till I feel that it is complete. This feeling that I have all the materials I need, and the work is complete and ready to be shared with the world is something I have learned and developed over the years.

As a teenager, I was never quite sure when I had done enough to do justice to an idea. However, after a couple of decades, I just know instinctively, when a work is complete. This only comes after practicing the creators craft you are currently involved in over a long period of time. There are some people, who have been touched with that rare genius instinct and know at an early stage, when their work is complete.

You can develop your creator vision in a similar fashion and by watching other creators at work. It becomes so much simpler when you give in to your imagination and creativity and just allow your creative process to flow uninterrupted. When the gates to your creativity are opened, you will be one with the universal creative force and will be free to create your next masterpiece.

Travelling through Memories

There are moments in life,
When memories and images,
Fly fast and they fly by,
In the blink of an eye.
Travelling through memories,
Like old movies that run,
Under the pale moon and sun.
Memories of silver,
Dissolve under the pale moonlight.
Memories of gold,
Woven like cords of shining twine,
Are written with feeling and signs.
We travel through our memories,
Like we are in a plane or a train.
We carry our memories within our minds,
Not for any profit or for gain,
Our memories make our lives,
Filling us with joy to overcome pain.
Take a trip through your memories.
See every one of those movies,
With a sense of love and care.
They are your memories,
Filled with passion, love and pain.

Our memories make our lives,
They make our human history.
Memories are like threads of gold,
Revealing precious treasures untold.

The Journey of an Ordinary Book

The book was nothing special,
    The topic was making writing simple.
It was all about finding your mission,
To devote your life to write something.
The book was written by someone,
Who discovered the writer within.
The book was not about telling the reader,
How they should write and be a leader?
The book was an ordinary book,
Filled with a thousand seeds of ideas.
The author wanted a reader to find,
Ideas and stories of every variety and kind.
The journey of this ordinary book,
Was so very extraordinary.
A hundred new writers found their way,
They walk on the Writer's Way today.
This ordinary book written and shared,
Its words of wisdom with the world.
It travels through a million eager hands,
To help them write their own literary plans.

The Book of Green Leaves

E very leaf tells its story.
　　One that is filled with sadness and glory.
A story that will be told for centuries,
One that is embedded into the trees.
Every tree that stands today,
Has been a witness to this show.
This performance that nature displays,
Has been done in a million replays.
Every leaf on every tree,
Is a living appendage with its destiny.
It has a time to be green and alive,
It has a time to be joyful and thrive.
The book of green leaves on this earth,
Tell the story of creation from birth.
This book can never be stolen be thieves,
It can be read by anyone who believes.

The Gods Must be Crazy

There is pollution,
	There is deforestation,
There is contamination,
There is extinction.
The Gods must be crazy,
To allow this to happen.
As the world turns,
As we humans sigh,
A tear forms in the eyes of Gods,
As they watch us cry.
There is global warming,
There are population explosions,
There is scarcity and poverty,
The Gods must be crazy,
To allow all this to happen.
As the Sun rises,
As the Sun sets,
Every day is a new beginning,
This is a gift given by the Gods,
A type of heavenly reward.
There are landslides,
There are earthquakes,
There are floods that wash villages away.
The Gods must be crazy,

To allow these terrible things to happen.
We know that we will see another day,
The Gods are on our side.
The Gods must be crazy and kind,
They try to always protect us,
Our lives, hearts and our minds.

The Gods must be having a Laugh

There are wars,
  There is destruction.
There is great wealth,
There is greater poverty.
There are cures for illnesses,
There are even higher deaths,
As humans kill other humans.
The Gods must be having a laugh,
As humans lose their minds.
The Gods must be watching amused,
As humans have freedom confused,
To live their lives so recklessly,
As they battle their own fragility.
There is in the world segregation,
That feeling of division and separation,
From the rest of the congregation.
The Gods must be having a laugh,
As they watch the world go bananas.
There is hatred and there is violence,
There are cries that shatter the silence.
Humans hurts other humans without care,
Love, peace and forgiveness are so rare.
There are talks for peace and harmony,

But all we see is discord and disharmony.
The Gods must be having a laugh,
As they watch the humanity charade.
There is no love between human beings,
In this ongoing living dynamic cartoon parade.
There are only words of peace, love and charity,
While war and violence are what the Gods can see.

Dream of a Bonsai Tree

I t was a busy, tiring day,
　　Nothing seemed to be going her way.
Even after all the effort and the work,
She was not receiving a promotion or a perk.
Every project that came her way,
She tried to complete in every way.
Every challenge she faced with skill,
She would not give up or give in.
For the last ten years she gave her all,
However, she was hitting a solid brick wall.
That night as she closed her eyes,
She wished she could soar to the skies.
She wished that she achieved her success,
To be triumphant and to progress.
That night she had a peaceful dream,
As she sat beside a tranquil stream.
An old monk came to her with a gift,
A small bonsai tree, that he could lift.
The well-formed tree was so rare,
That she could not help but silently stare.
The tree was so lovingly shaped and green,
A more perfect specimen was never seen.
She awoke the next day and forgot her dream,
As reality hit her life, at that stream,

She forgot about the bonsai tree dream,
The gift she got at the Tranquil stream,
It was only when her luck began to change,
That she remembered her dream of the tree,
It was bringing her peace, wealth, and harmony.
She changed her job and her home,
To enjoy life and to be free to roam.
She got a new job as a happiness coach,
With a hundred bonsai trees on her front porch.
She found love, harmony, joy, and romance,
Her life was now a graceful and beautiful dance.
Every day she pruned and shaped her bonsai trees,
As wisdom and wishes were carried on the breeze.
Her dream of the bonsai tree,
Was wrapped in peace and harmony.

Halloween Photography

The darkness descends on the city, the homes are all lit, and the streets are empty. An eerie whisper is heard in the trees as the wind whistles and moves past the windows, through the branches, over rooftops, and sweeping across cemeteries and abandoned churches.

There is no movement anywhere in the city. The townspeople are afraid and shiver in fear in their homes. The curtains are drawn, and the light is subdued. The streetlights appear to dim, as a dark presence flows past the city gates.

The whispering breeze, sweeps across the dark and gloomy cemeteries, moving the fallen leaves as if to clear the way for nocturnal visitors. There is a sudden movement to be seen in the shadows of the dark streets, as a group of city photographers makes their way in silence to view the city on a dark and evil Halloween night. It is a small group of three men, two are elderly and one is a young man, there are two elderly women with large cameras and a young woman with a sophisticated camera on her shoulder. These Halloween photographers are out to capture the spirits that float and fly in the night.

The graveyards have come alive, like the streets, as tiny, ghosts, ghouls, witches, and goblins start knocking door to door for trick-o-treats, under the light of the several jack-o-lanterns which have seemingly come alive like magic.

Skeletal fingers creep out from the dark graveyard soil, as more of these skeletal visitors arrive to attend the ceremony of ghosts and ghouls on that dark and long Halloween. While all this is taking place a group of young men is watching the latest Batman animated movie, "The Long Halloween", based on the graphic novel of the same name. You can only look at the darkness of the night, in the absence of light.

Voices of Generations

Things are going to change,
There are good times ahead.
The best is yet to come,
Let us look towards the Sun.
The voices of generations,
Speak their wisdom down the ages.
Those voices are now muffled,
As we progress in evolutionary stages.
Everything is falling apart,
Don't make the same mistakes we did.
Once the pandora box is open,
There is no way to close the lid.
The voices of generations,
All felt the world was falling apart,
The days were dark and everything fell,
Everyone and everything was going to hell.
Decades and years have come and gone,
New generations have died and been reborn.
The world and mankind move cautiously ahead,
A brighter dawn lies light years ahead.

Overcome Fear to find Courage

I t could be fear,
　　That holds you back in life.
It could be fear,
That stops you from moving ahead.
Go and claim what is your due,
By discovering the real you.
If you need a new job,
You will need a new skill too.
Go and learn what needs to be done,
Retrain and become a better you.
Overcome your fear doing something new,
Your life is your own it is so very true.
You want to learn to drive,
To want to learn to ride a horse.
Do what needs to be done,
To be a driver or a horse rider.
Overcome your fear and know,
That the world is outside your door.
Overcome the fear inside,
By pushing boundaries every day.
Step out of your comfort zonc,
Do new things and visit new places,
Step into the meditation zone.

The real you, needs to be free,
Overcoming fear is the powerful key.

Hang On One Minute Longer

As a teenager and in my twenties, I wanted to quit so many things that seemed difficult. It was at these times, that I remembered a proverb I had seen in a book I read at school. The proverb was something about a hero hanging on a minute longer.

I later knew that I just had to find the full proverb, as it was something that I needed to adopt. I looked everywhere and then the internet happened. It was so much easier finding the exact wording of the quote.

The proverb was of Norwegian origin, and it stated, "Heroism consists of hanging on one minute longer." Yes, this was something that seemed to speak to me. I had no intention of playing the hero or doing anything heroic in life. When anything got difficult for me, like understanding a new subject, doing a new type of work, or starting a new project, I would think of giving up. Perhaps it was time for me to change direction and take up a new interest. On the other hand, I could just stick to what I was doing and give it a chance.

As time went on, I found that by keeping on in trying to understand a new subject, doing a new job, or starting a new project, I did succeed by sticking to what I was doing. It was my opportunity to be a hero, to who I was as an individual and to give myself an opportunity to evolve, as a creative individual, capable of facing the challenges of life.

Have You Lost Your Head?

H ave you felt like you have lost your head?
    You just want to keep writing, never stopping.
The ideas just keep flowing and you love it,
You do not want to stop it and spoil it.
It is a great feeling to be in touch,
With the universe of boundless creativity.
Every spoken word, sight, and sound,
Creates a world of ideas in an instant.
A wealth of ideas you have found,
Waiting to materialize in your creations,
Every work being a special celebration.
Have you lost your head?
No, I am bursting with creativity.
Who needs a head to think logically,
When you are bursting with imagination,
With a large powerhouse of creativity.
An ocean of ideas stretches to eternity,
The more you use these whispers,
The more they seem to grow and multiply,
As one creation is released to the world,
Another gets its wings and is ready to fly.
They may ask if you have lost your head?
That is not true it can be said.

You are flying high on octane,
You are flying on the wings of propane,
You are flying on the back of imagination,
You are flying in creative jubilation.
Have you lost your head?
No, I am bursting with creativity.
Who needs a body and a head,
To rest on a pillow in a warm bed,
When you are a creative flame,
Flying on your imagination in eternity.
Who needs a weary body,
When you are alive and awake,
Fuelled by the power of creativity,
As you write from dusk till dawn,
Listening to your muse in serenity.

Locked in a Memoir

What have you collected?
What memories have you found?
Were they happy memories?
A few sad ones too,
That brough tears like morning dew.
A few that were hard to write,
Everything being honest and true.
Locked in a memoir for all time,
Preserved in pages like a silken rhyme.
As you sat down to write,
The memoir of your exciting life,
Did you smile, laugh and cry?
As you watched happy memories,
Rise to the surface and softly fly.
While the sad ones hurt you inside,
A pain that is not easy to hide.
Collect your life's experiences,
Carefully and write them down.
There are some memories locked away,
Deep within the landscape of your mind,
While others roam free for all time.
Those memories that have not seen,
The light of a bright and summer day,
Will also come out to play today.

Keep all your memories in your memoir,
All the experiences that you have enjoyed,
The painful ones that you have endured.
Your heart is exposed in your memoir,
To be read by generations to come,
With your wisdom of life's passing hour.
You are locked in your memoir for all time,
To be celebrated by readers like a joyful rhyme.

Chronicling a life in a Memoir

Every life that has been lived, that is being lived and which will be lived in the future will make an interesting memoir for readers. Have you thought about writing down your life story, filled with your life experiences and adorned with your wisdom?

A life is chronicled in a memoir, by the person who has lived and learned so much in that life. Great men and women have written about their lives, about all that they have experienced, including their failures and their successes. There are those who have risen from poverty to become men and women who have changed history. There are also memoirs written by those, who have fallen from grace, yet who have managed to turn their lives around to take their place in the spotlight once again.

What can we learn by reading the memoirs of famous and common people? We can gain the wisdom that they have to share in their words and experiences. We can enter their lives and step into the world that they inhabit or have inhabited during their lifetimes. Historical personalities have so much to share with us, about their lives, loves, failures and triumphs.

We must always remember that the famous people of yesterday and today, were once common people like you and I. You do not have to be a popular personality to write the memoir of your life. Chronicle your life in a memoir starting today and you will find that your life has been more interesting than you can imagine and you have so much to share with readers, who enjoy reading and learning from memoirs.

Gentle Reminders

On dark days and cold nights,
We fail to rise to dizzying heights.
When we have disappointments,
Failures and depression as companions,
We are reminded that all is not lost.
Every battle won has a dreadful cost.
The sun rises the next day,
A new day begins in every way.
There is a chance for trying once again.
Life is for overcoming distress and pain.
A good opportunity maybe lost for all time.
Night comes after day every time.
There are more opportunities,
Abundant chances for new destinies.
Nature informs us that there is hope,
It helps us to be brave and to cope.
A river of hope helps us to dream,
Life is mystery and magic it does seem.
We are tried and we are tested,
Burnished in the flames like metal.
We are shaped and formed by our will.
Yet we do not stumble or fall,
We strive to stand above it all.
Like a rainbow that comes after the rain,

There is always calm after the pain.
Listen to the gentle lessons of nature zen,
Fall into a trance of love at the count of ten.
Present in the seasons, and in time,
Captured in the lines of this rhyme.

Worlds Apart and in Love

L ove does not wait,
    Love does not run,
Love just happens so suddenly,
When you find the right one.
Love can happen at any time,
Love can happen for anyone.
Love can be so unexpected,
Striking in winter or a summer sun.
Love can cross oceans and seas,
Love is more than just birds and bees.
Love is the thunder in the heart,
United in love though worlds apart.
Love is a miracle waiting to happen,
Love is beyond pain, passion and original sin.
Poets have sung about the power of love,
Filled with Cupid's potion from above.

Legacy of Generations

The work that we do today,
  Started many years ago,
By our ancestors of old.
Their history has gone cold.
The items we see in the world,
Have been created so many years ago.
Whatever talents and skills we have today,
Have been passed down the generations,
From the past to our present day.
Our ancestors made a difference,
Though they were not sure they did.
Whatever we can create and do today,
Is now also engraved into our DNA.
Within each one of us lies the seed,
The legacy of our generations,
Passed down to each one of us.
Embrace your talents and every skill,
It is your legacy that powers your will.
Within you is the legacy of generations,
Of those who have lived and loved before.
Honour their memory by being the best you can.
Make a difference in the world, that is the plan.

Legacy of Humanity

They made the buildings,
    They made the roads.
They put systems in place,
They even went to outer space.
Our world of brick and mortar,
Was built by the sweat of millions.
Our world of culture and society,
Is enjoyed today by billions.
The Earth we inhabit is witness,
To every footstep and every kiss.
Our world has seen generations,
Come and go in all nations.
The legacy of humanity has been,
To build a better and brighter future,
For the generations to come and enjoy.
New people and new workers to employ.
The generations that have long gone,
Laid our present and strong foundation,
In every land and every great nation.
The legacy of humanity is for posterity.

A Poem about Making Money Online

A million people search every time,
    About making money online.
Everyone wants to start a side hustle,
One that is easy and interesting,
Which does not require too much muscle.
There are so many ways to make money online,
That do not require you to visit the office,
All it needs is the internet and phone line.
There are ways to make money online,
From auctions, to affiliate marketing of items,
Selling products for companies for commission.
Making short videos on YouTube,
From coaching, cooking, lifestyle advice,
That requires no payment or permission.
You can make money online starting today,
By writing and self-publishing e-books,
From fiction to healthy eating and recipe books.
Anyone can start making money online,
By making and selling products on Etsy,
From bags, to candles, to prints,
To paintings of beautiful scenery.
Make money online today and every day,
By writing articles, poems and stories,

By becoming a freelance designer or movie-maker.
There are so many ways to make money online,
That do not require you to visit the office,
All it needs is the internet and phone line.
There are no limits to what you can do,
To make money online today.
From art, to cooking, to gardening,
To writing, coaching, it all does pay.
A million people search every time,
About making money online.
Everyone wants to start a side hustle,
One that is easy and interesting,
Which does not require too much muscle.

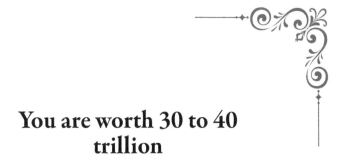

You are worth 30 to 40 trillion

We are in the habit of always thinking about the value of objects in currency. The currency can be dollars, pounds, yen or even in cryptocurrency. We work, we earn and then we spend what we earn to live a decent life, for our families, ourselves and for contributing to society.

If we see something we like we want to buy it, so we use our currency to get us what we want to make life more comfortable. We know the worth of an object by the value it represents in human created currency. Currency is important for our civilizations to survive. The economy needs currency, assets, reserves, resources, infrastructures for all that comes with cities, towns, villages and world economies.

You are worth 30 to 40 trillion human blood cells. Every human body is composed of 30 to 40 trillion cells, though scientists are still not sure about the exact number. Though most of the cells of the human body are red blood cells. Every cell is vital for your existence if one is missing there are complications. Your wealth is what makes you complete in our world.

With the present advancements in science and technology, there may come a time when we will all be wealthy for who we are as individuals. So, what is your wealth apart from all the money you may have and the assets you own. Your imagination, your creativity, your life, your work, your skills, your family and all that you create, make and inspire in this world is your wealth.

You are richer than Midas and unlike that unfortunate man who turned whatever, he touched to gold, your intrinsic value as an individual is your wealth, which can make this life more positive, productive and fulfilling.

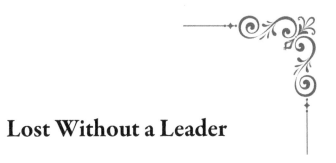

Lost Without a Leader

The people always looked up to their leader. That one person who could show them the way out of the darkness. That one person who had the wisdom to guide them through the toughest days and the coldest nights.

The leader was the person who had trained all his or her life to learn as much as he could about the good and bad, the happy and the sad, the negative and the positive forces of the world. When the leader first took up the sceptre, he was ready, for when the people chose him as their leader. The leader had the power and the vision to lead his or her people out of the darkness into the wonders of the light.

It was a dark day and a darker night when the leader lost his battle with the forces of evil. The people were lost, the company was sliding into ruin. The employees would be without jobs, as the enterprise would fail. It was at that moment of crisis when from among the followers one man decided to save the company and the teams who depended on the job for their livelihoods.

Without a leader, followers need to stand up for what they believe in. As a united group, with a powerful leader, a group can accomplish anything in life. If you happen to be a person who is a follower, it is time to find the leader within. Every enterprise needs a leader and every leader needs a group to lead towards a brighter future.

Albums of Memories

We create albums of memories,
Without ever knowing it,
We create movies of memories,
Every frame we know it.
Every day we fill these albums,
With pictures and emotions.
These are not lost memories,
They are filled with our passions.
Albums of memories we grow,
Locked away in our hearts,
Stored in our fertile minds.
They all play their parts.
Pages of emotions come alive,
By everything we do and say,
Albums of memories are treasures,
We enjoy them every single day.

Snippets of Days

Do you remember yesterday,
    Do you remember every day?
Our minds are filled with memories
Just snippets of days we have lived.
Glimpses of days we can see,
Like ripples on a dark sea.
We see the shadows of days,
We find comfort in our memories.
We remember moments of love,
We recall times of sorrow and pain.
Snippets of days, months, and years,
Pass through our minds once again.
Today will be a snippet,
A fragment of a memory tomorrow.
Our albums of memories,
Make us who we are today.
Preserve your albums of memories,
View them in quiet times,
View them to gain inspiration.
Those memories are your victories,
Your pains, your joys and celebration.

She came in his Dreams

Every night as he went to sleep,
He would step into his dream.
Sara always appeared in his dreams,
A woman he had never seen.
Who was this woman in his dream?
Who was this woman he wondered?
He knew her name and she knew his.
She would show him a gold painted box,
With the words "Treasure Inside", inscribed.
What was this treasure in his dreams?
Tom had this dream every day of the week.
Where was this treasure he had to seek?
He looked high and low in his home,
He could not find a box of gold,
Which he wanted to touch and to hold.
One summer afternoon when he was at home,
He went to clear out his attic on his own.
In the attic he found a box of wood,
Filled with his father's precious stamps of old.
This was the box of gold with treasures untold.
A fortune he made once they were by auction sold.
Who was the woman in his dreams?
A woman of such beauty he had never seen.
One day she walked into his florist shop,

To pick up a flower bouquet for her mother.
She looked at him and he gazed at her that night,
They were kindred souls and it was love at first sight.

Speak to me from the shadows of my dreams

WHEN IN THE REALM OF dreams,
We can do so many amazing things.
We can conjure up the most wonderful things,
While appreciating all that imagination brings.
In that state of solitude and slumber,
We allow our troubled minds to wander.
In the Kingdom of the sleeping souls,
We can walk on soft clouds and on hot coals.
In my dream I ask my mentors and my guide,
To help me on my quest as I take this ride.
"Guide me great mentors and my honest guide,
Through this world from which we cannot hide."
"Speak to me wise mentors and loyal guide,
Show me how our fears we always hide.
Help me to overcome whatever holds me back,
To improve myself and make up for any lack."
From the shadows of my million dreams,
There are lands where truth shines and gleams.
A hundred voices speak, but there is one voice for me,
The strong voice of wisdom guiding me to tranquillity.

Every Video Game is a Story

We all know what gamers look like. They are those children and teenagers, who are obsessed with their phones and gaming consoles. They are absorbed by what they are looking at on their screens and monitors. Gamers do not have the time for conversations or to interact in the real world with friends and family. Yet, they have friends online and gaming friends, opponents they share their ideas and communicate with constantly. I am not a gamer, but would love to be one, if I had the time.

Children, young people and the middle-aged individuals who grew up with gaming, are obsessed and will always be passionate about their games. Gamers are always on the lookout for the new Xbox and the PS5 consoles. These individuals are the first to buy the latest gaming consoles when they are released or "dropped". These gamers are willing to shell out lots of cash for the latest games that are released in the marketplace. Every gamer is aware of the latest games. I just know a few of the games like Call of Duty, Minecraft, Roblox, Assassin's Creed, Hogwarts, Arkham Asylum, Evil West, Hellblade, Sniper Elite 4 and the list continues to grow.

What are these games and why are they so popular? These games usually involve one character, who has to begin the game, go through a lot of hurdles and overcome several obstacles along the way, to get the prize at the end. Video Gamers progress from the first level to the next level which has tougher tests that need to be completed, to get the points at the end.

Video games are popular among gamers because of the simple fact that they are stories being told and the player is taking an active part. You as the gamer need to achieve certain goals to get the prize at the end. Every game places the gamer in a situation where he or she has to make a quick decision, for example to fight the enemy or to flee in haste. The mind of the gamer is in sync with the story taking place in the fantasy world of the game. The video gamer is a character the story.

The people who develop the game are in fact master storytellers. They create characters both good or bad for the players of the game. Every character has his or her strengths and weaknesses. Game Creators are Storytellers and writers of interesting, yet powerful stories with memorable storylines. The world of gaming is always on the lookout for writers to write stories and to write about video games. Games are so popular with gamers, because the story writers and game crafters keep the players interested and engaged in the game. A video game is like an unputdownable novel. Do you have an idea for the next popular video game? Do a course in writing for video games and yo may make a fortune in the future as a game writer.

https://www.polygon.com/features/2019/1/10/18165611/how-to-write-a-video-game-story-narrative-building-tips

The Call to Create

H ave you felt the strength of an idea? It is a feeling that makes you want to create something. Whether it is an idea or just a feeling, you want to create that which you imagine in your mind. The visualization of an idea gives it power and makes you create an artistic piece.

It could be a song, a poem, a piece of art or short story, yet you must create that which you have in your mind. We are all called to create something of value in this life. We are creators from the time of creation. Mankind created the fire that fuelled civilizations, the wheels of industry that helped in the advancement of humanity, the technology that harnesses the power to transform the human race.

It is the same passion that fuels life, that is the secret of creation. That urge to create machines, art, sculptures, medicine, artificial intelligence is in our DNA. We are all children of creation and possess that powerful gene to create wondrous marvels, using the power of our imagination and creativity.

Discover you creator gene, by doing what you enjoy in life, from making your favourite cocktail, building a piece of furniture, writing a poem, or composing a melody. Listen to the call to create and you will discover the power that fuels your cosmic energies that reside within your soul.

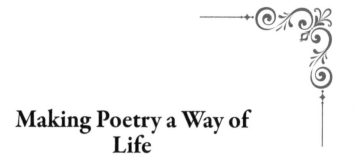

Making Poetry a Way of Life

I like to imagine that everyone spoke like William Shakespeare, during the time he was writing his wonderful plays. That is simply not true, because ordinary people speak like ordinary people do, without all the colourful words and fanciful language. Every age will have its great and wise storytellers and poets, who create worlds wonderful and rare, with characters beyond compare.

In the old days the poets would get together at the weekend, to recite their wonderful rhyme, each better than the other. It was time for good fun and competition, while they enjoyed the company of their literary friends. The Sunday poetry club, was a gift for every poet from above. It was an opportunity to express their ideas, to let the world share their poetic rhymes, to win their war of expressive words every time.

In the days of old, a poet's words were more precious than gold. In the days that have come and gone, every poet would tell the most wonderful stories in his ballads and express the words of love in his sonnets. The words of Sunday Poets echoes in the hearts and in minds of the people who enjoy reading and writing poetry today.

The poets of today, who come together at the Sunday Poetry club, have the chance to maintain the tradition of poetry, the love and the power of poetry in the world. The Sunday poets nurture the love of poetry in society and you are welcome to create your online or offline poetry club, for some great slam poetry or performance poetry.

Whether you write poems or perform them this is your chance to make poetry a force to reckon with in this age of artificial intelligencc and genetic advancement. Let powerful and passionate poetry become the next stage of human evolution and development.

The Dinner Invitation

Hector and his family,
    Were excited that evening.
There was laughter, dancing and singing.
Hector felt like a lottery ticket winner.
His wife Hilary and his two small children,
Were invited out to a very special dinner.
Hector's boss Viktor,
Invited the family to his home,
To have a meal and spend time,
To eat delicious dishes,
While drinking fine wine.
Viktor was a good boss,
He was the ideal type of guy,
Polite, respectful, and upright.
A kind boss who would comfort,
His employees if he saw them cry.
Hector's two little children Jack and Mary,
Ate all the food on their plates,
They even tried the custard and dates.
Hector and Viktor chatted and laughed,
While their wives Hilary and Rebecca,
Spent the evening discussing their lives,
As friends, companions, lovers, and wives.
After a hearty meal Hector and his family,

Left Viktor's home happy and bright,
They all had a good sleep that night.
It was only the next day,
When Hector went into work,
He found his life thrown into disarray,
Viktor and the company had moved away.
Hector had to rebuild his life once again,
He became a driver on an electric train.

The reflections on Crystal Lake

It was a clear blue crystal lake,
　　When he was just a young boy.
He had wonderful memories,
Spent fishing and wishing on that lake.
He spent many days with his friends,
Playing at the lake when summer never ends.
The young couples spent their evenings,
Sitting down in romantic bliss.
Having their first, second and seventh kiss,
Or sitting in small boats on the waters.
Parents watched their children play,
It was ideal for their sons and daughters.
The children of this town loved the lake,
Till a young child went alone and drowned in it.
The children were banned from using it.
The lake was closed from further use,
Abandoned and desolate it lay for years,
It was forgotten in the dust and the tears.
Ten years later John returned to the town,
He was going to restore the lake,
To its former magnificence, power and glory.
It took two months to clean the waters,
Of all the dirt, the grime and the slime.

The waters of crystal lake shone bright,
As it reflected the silver moonlight.
The waters of crystal lake were alive,
As it reflected the heavens on its surface,
There was joy and a smile on every face.
The white statue of a young boy,
Throwing a stone into the lake,
Was placed near the edge of the waters,
In remembrance of the lad who lost his life.
A welcome sight for the people of the town,
Jack was gone but he was never forgotten.
Restoring crystal lake was the best decision,
It was a miracle to behold in every reflection.
As every bird flew over the lake and stretched its wing,
The lives around the town of crystal lake kept changing.
That lake of clear blue was back to its glory,
We now conclude this simple and lovely story.

The Heatwave is coming to Britain

Next week is going to be a sunny week,
 The sun will scorch the earth at its peak.
Is this the global warning sign,
With the weather worldwide in decline?
The Heatwave comes to Britain,
Will it be followed by high tide and rain?
The land will be under warm sunny skies,
As the heat will bring tears to our eyes.
The Earth is warming day by day,
As the scientists and meteorologists say.
The warm days will give way to thunder and rain,
In the land it will be even warmer than Spain.
It will be wise to complete work and retire,
As the heat will soar, while we perspire.
Water will not satisfy our unquenchable thirst,
Like dry cracked Earth under a cloud burst.
Our world is undergoing a climate change,
From the seas to the mountain range.
We need to reclaim our forests once again,
To ensure that we get sufficient rain.
We need to clean our waters, rivers and lakes,
To save our planet and doing whatever it takes.
Our Earth needs to be green once again,

So the plants can be nourished in purifying rain.
We need to clean and detoxify our atmosphere,
So that the sky is blue and the air is clear.
The heat is coming in waves to Britain,
Followed by storms, winds and pouring rain.
Cool waters from the heavens will cool the Earth,
As nature and humanity rejoice in their mirth.
The temperatures are rising across the planet,
Attracting heat like a spinning magnet.
The only way to stop every heatwave,
Is by informing greedy humanity to behave.
Britain is going to be warmer than Morocco,
As the rivers turn to streams while they flow.
The land of the Royals is parched and cracked,
Like water flowing off a camel's back.
The green plants will be unable to thrive,
With water scarcity greenery will barely survive.
The land of the Castles, Kings and Knights,
Will experience scorching heat from day to night.
Next week is going to be a very hot week,
The sun will scorch the earth at its peak.
Is this the global warning sign,
With the weather worldwide in decline.
The Heatwave comes to Britain,
Will it be followed by high tide and rain?

Growing wealth like a Money Tree

Planting seeds and growing trees,
        Was his gifts and his natural skill,
He could make a sapling sprout into a tree,
They called him the father of every tree,
There was no better gardener than Rodney.
As a child he could not study much,
He preferred playing in the garden,
Carefully removing the roots of the weeds,
Gently placing new productive seeds.
As the years passed and Rodney grew,
To be a strong young man he found,
That he was popular growing seeds in the ground.
Gardening helped him to grow his wealth,
It kept him fit and in the pink of health.
Rodney grew his wealth like a money tree,
It made him popular; it was his destiny.
The plants grew in leaps and in bounds,
A better plant whisperer could not be found.
Turning the world greener was his mission,
Saving forest and trees was his decision.
If you are passionate for a hobby,
You will most definitely find,
That it will help you to enjoy life,

With all that peace of mind.

Avoiding the News

A re you guilty of not following the news?
There are a number of us who avoid the news, including myself, due to its repetitive nature. There are also many who have stopped watching the news, as it is too depressing. We read the headlines of all that is happening in the world, voluntarily or involuntarily, this is due to the presence of social media today.

Messages and news about the world and what is happening around us is constantly filtering into our minds, whether we want to accept them or not. In my opinion, we are constantly being bombarded by the news of the world, which we cannot control, unless a person lives in a cave on a mountain-top cut away from society and civilization.

Are you like myself guilty of not following the news of what is happening in the world around us? I have noticed that we do not have to open a newspaper or read a news item on social media to know what is happening in the world. Our brains are equipped to absorb information quickly and process that information faster.

While we are checking emails and doing our work on the internet, we are also absorbing the news snippets that keep appearing. So, whether we want to or not, we are definitely in touch with the news every day. This is one reason that accounts for the repetitive nature of the news. Negative news and information is displayed repeatedly online for us to view, as we browse the web while doing our professional or personal work and skill development. We are are news readers and listeners whether we like it or not. Thank you for reading this article about avoiding reading or listening to the news.

https://www.thevibes.com/articles/world/63421/growing-numbers-avoiding-news-as-too-depressing-report

Use Your Power of Love

We do not realize,
That we have the power,
Which quietly resides within,
Every person in the world.
Harness and release the power of love,
That flows into you from the cosmos above.
We have the power to love,
We are capable of so much love,
We are born to show love.
Take the superpower of your love,
Overcome all that brings strife.
Use the silent dynamo of love within you,
Watch miracles happen in your life,
As all that you desire,
Is magnetically drawn to you.
Your power of love,
Is the largest reservoir,
Filled with the energy of love,
Simply waiting to be turned on.
Open the gates to the power,
That enormous burst of love,
Which will transform you,
Bringing magic into all you do.
Harness and release the power of love,

That flows into you from the cosmos above.
We are all superheroes with superpowers,
We have strong values, strengths and emotions,
We are the children of the cosmos and the stars.

Using the Power of Gratitude

We forget to be grateful in life.
Even when we get rewards.
We have good fortune and abundance.
We still forget to be grateful,
For all the things we receive in life.
Use the Power of Gratitude,
To get more harmony in life.
Harness the power of being thankful,
To realize the richness of your life.
When good things happen to us,
We just take them for granted.
Remember all the good things,
That make your life fun.
Recall those happy times,
All those golden memories,
They are the treasures of life,
Which you are grateful to have,
Which mean so much to you.
Start your day with a large dose,
Of gratitude as your attitude.
Go through your day with a smile,
Even after you have walked a mile.
Gratitude is your superpower,

That can grow every hour,
Like a garden for your home,
All your gratefulness brings forth,
Gratitude flowers every abundant hour.

Take the Power of Creativity

The power of creativity,
    Will keep your mind,
Filled with ideas every day.
The power of creativity,
Will help you to discover,
A world of inspiring ideas.
Unlock the power of creativity,
By appreciating life,
By finding the magic in life,
By looking for miracles,
In everything around, you.
The universe is made of ideas,
The same creative thoughts,
That made the stars and the universe,
Made you from a single cell.
Take the power of your creativity,
Fill your mind with imagination.
Create a world of your ideas,
Use your skills and talents to see,
The purpose of your life,
The path of your creative destiny.
The power of creativity,
Will always keep your mind free.

Constant use of your creativity,
Will unlock the universe of ideas,
That are yours to use for free.
Trust your imagination,
Believe in its power,
Watch it grow from a sapling,
To a mighty oak tree.
Your life is a product,
Of your imagination.
Discover the wisdom of your destiny,
In the life pages of your creativity.
The purpose of your life,
The path of your creative destiny.
The power of creativity,
Will always keep your mind free.

Use the Power of Positivity

E ven on the day,
    When nothing seems to work,
When everything seems wrong,
When you feel lost,
When you feel broken,
When you cannot find your way,
There is still positive power,
Deep within your being.
Create a positive mindset,
Focus on all that is good,
All feelings of hope, love and peace.
Condition your mind and heart,
To always look on the bright side,
Where negativity has nowhere to hide.
Build a powerhouse of positivity,
Deep within your heart and soul,
This reservoir of positive power,
Will make your life feel complete,
Will make your soul feel whole.
The Law of Attraction relies on you,
To firstly build your Bank,
With stacks of positive power,
In your mind, heart and soul.

The Law of Attraction,
A gift for us from the universe,
Thrives on the bank of positive power,
It will make your life richer,
Every day, every week and every hour.
Miracles will start to happen,
For you every day and in every way,
When you know that your positive power
Can create a positive reality for you,
From a dream home, a loving family,
To great wealth and a fancy car.
Take the power of positivity,
To remake your life and destiny,
To a fulfilled life here in the world,
Where anything is possible,
With the power of positivity.
Condition your mind and heart,
To always look on the bright side,
Where negativity has nowhere to hide.

Which Drumbeat Do You Follow?

"*You've always marched to the beat of your own drum, and I know you do things in your own time and your own way.*"
— *Alexa Riley*

We have all heard that quote, "Marching to the beat of his on drum", at some time over the years. It basically means that an individual does his own thing and does not follow the rules and regulations of anyone else. It also means that the person has his own opinion and does not get influenced by anyone else.

There was a time, when I was a teenager and in my twenties that what other people thought or said mattered to be. Over the years, I have learned that what other people thought or felt about my work, did not help me to grow as an individual. Constructive criticism is always good, and I would use it to improve my work. However, there are those who just criticize because it is the only thing they enjoy doing.

"*I always march to the beat of my own drum... I always have, ALWAYS will.*"

- *Samantha Fontien*

Whose drumbeat do you follow in life? Is it the opinions of family or friends that matter to you and you are willing to sacrifice what you believe in life? The opinions of others keep changing, one day they will tell you that what you do is great, the next day they will say that your work is just terrible. This brings a smile or a smirk to my face, because over the years, I have found that this is so true.

In my opinion and after having lived for a number of years listening to and marching to my own drumbeat, I can say that it is the best way to find happiness. If you prefer listening to and following the opinions of others in life, it is great, if you are happy. However, if there comes a time when you need to stand up for what you believe in life and beat your own path, then start living life on your terms.

Homeward Bound

We love setting out to new places,
We look forward to new experiences,
We want to see new cultures,
Try out new exotic cuisine,
Never heard of or seen.
We capture our trips and holidays,
In photos and in video clips.
We have great memories,
From all these wonderful trips.
Up mountains and down the stream,
We enjoy the holiday dream.
Home is where the heart resides,
A safe place to close tired eyes.
At the end of every holiday,
We look forward to the last trip,
When we pack up our holidays,
We set off to where we started from.
Our feet are now back on home ground,
We are now set to be homeward bound.
Our holiday life has come right around,
We circle back to be homeward bound.
We are tired, we can sleep safe and sound,
We are heading back; we are homeward bound.

The Best Slice of Your Life

The first day at school,
    Which you felt was so cool.
Your wedding day with your love,
A match made from above.
The birth of your child,
Who grows up sane or just wild.
Your first job and first salary,
Which made you afford cake and tea.
Which day is the best day of your life?
The day that everything was just ideal,
Like a well-prepared wholesome meal.
The birthday cake was out of this world,
With cream, chocolate, and edible pearls.
The wedding cake was of perfect design,
Toasted with white and rich red wine.
All the delicious cakes over the years,
Eaten with meals and with cold beers.
There is just one slice that you love best,
Which is by far your very best.
What is the best slice of your life,
When everything was just as it should be,
Your happiness was as boundless as eternity.
It is that special day when life was ideal,

When you can recall how you did feel.
The best slice of your life is in your heart,
Filled with feelings never to part.
Even when days are grim, cloudy and grey,
Your best slice of life will with you always stay.
Enjoy the memories of that special time,
With all the joy, love, cake and wine.

The Sum of Life with Additions and Subtractions

The recipe of life
Is something we need,
Something we would like to have.
To overcome hardships and strife.
The ingredients of life,
From the flowers of beauty,
To the most fruitful seed,
Will overcome the deadliest weed,
Is something we would love to have,
T make our lives complete.
Life is composed of so much more,
Like a bounty of a well-stocked store.
There are so many additions,
There are so many subtractions.
Add all the positive feelings and vibes,
With the cheerful drums beats of tribes.
Subtract all the negative emotions,
Give in to peace and solemn devotions.
The sum of life,
With all its beautiful additions,
With all its ugly subtractions,
Makes this life colourfully complete.

The totality of our life,
Is both bitter and so sweet.
It is this balanced harmony,
Which makes life complete.

Our Gods Will Not Protect Us

Time goes so very fast,
  Time goes so very slow.
Seasons come so quick and fast,
Seasons quietly disappear and go.
Rain falls from the heavens,
Thunder rolls across dark skies.
Lightning flashes from the heavens,
As the moon shines for our eyes.
The Gods will not protect us,
When there is thunder and rain.
The Gods will not save us,
From heartache and pain.
When rain floods valleys and cities,
Destroying land and helpless lives,
The Gods have abandoned us yet again,
As we endure our fragile mortal pain.
Our Gods will not protect us,
When the Earth is crushed like an atom,
As it collides with asteroids from space.
Our Gods will just turn their backs again.
They do not approve violence and vengeance.
We must save ourselves with our intelligence,
To use the gifts given to us by the Gods in space,

So that we save ourselves and our human race.

A Random Life- Is not random at all

L ife seems to be so random,
    Things happen with no reason.
Life is not really random at all,
With a fixed time for every season.
You are born at a particular time,
You live life fully every time in rhyme.
Things seems to happen by chance,
From falling in love and romance.
You study in a certain school,
Choosing all the right subjects.
You find the right or wrong employment,
It could be the office or a job at the Mint.
You live your random life so randomly,
From beginning, as a child to the very end.
Yet everything is not random in the end,
It is all well calculated my good friend.

The Mystery of Life

L ife is an interactive experience.
    One that we are undergoing every day.
Constantly receiving ideas from everywhere,
Developing complex lives of love and care.
The mystery of life reveals itself,
In every day that we live and breathe.
Every life is about adapting to change,
To one that takes care of every need.
Our minds are filled with new ideas,
Which we use or misuse by choice.
Life is about making every decision.
Fulfilling our dreams and our vision.
The mystery of life can be understood,
When we cherish every moment for good.
We are becoming more by learning and living,
Knowing that life is about receiving and giving.

Everyone is a Storyteller

There are stories we hear,
    There are stories we know.
Listening to great stories,
Is how we learn and grow.
There are legends and myths,
Those that tell us tall tales.
There are folklores and ballads,
Great stories akin to literary salads.
We are all storytellers,
Whether we want to be or not.
We all weave stories of silver and gold,
About lives courageous, fearsome and bold.
Every myth was created in a mind,
Of a human of a very special kind.
The Storyteller saw the seed of the myth,
Knowing that it would grow to become a hit.
Dreams have evolved into great stories,
Powerful legends that have seen the light.
Nightmares have been captured in story,
Savage, violent, brutal and bloody gory.
Everyone is a born Storyteller,
Planting the seeds of stories everywhere.
Weaving stories of joy and stories for shedding tears.
Is what Storytellers have been doing over the years.

Living the Story, a Chapter at a Time

If your life could be made into a movie,
    What would you call it and why?
You could put a fancy label onto it,
It could be an international box-office hit.
You are living the story every day,
Your days are the chapters in your life.
Every day has its beginning, middle and end,
Every challenge comes with something you defend.
This life is the story of you and only you.
It is the story of what has been and could be,
Your life is the epic, the legend and the mystery,
You are writing and rewriting your destiny.
Your life unfolds in every chapter lived,
With all you have taken and all that you have given.
The story of this life of yours is filled with miracles,
Opportunities, failures, successes and strong wills.
You are the messenger of your great story.
You are the character in every possible time.
You make the story a testament of your life,
Every time you can triumph over strife.

Artificial Neural
Network of Writers

Every thought in the human brain is a neuron that pulses with energy and transfers that information across the biological neural network. With the advancement of technology, scientists have created artificial neural networks (ANN) that can communicate with one another like the human brain.

As writers, poets, artists and creatives we are now able to exchange information without leaving our homes. Thanks to the creation, development and the advancement of technology, we communicate across large distances, cities, countries and oceans. This has resulted in the birth and the creation of the ultimate neural network of writers who exchange their ideas, comments, suggestions and contribute their literary creations.

Every piece of work that is produced and sent out across the artificial neural network of a publishing platform is a thought that is sent out to other writers and readers. The lines of communication, conversation, ideas, work and concepts are like neurons in the brain firing electrical impulses across the world.

As a fellow writer and reader, you are now receiving my thoughts in this article, while you are forming your own reactions to the content. We are similar to the brain sending and receiving information, while absorbing what we want and rejecting what we feel we do not need.

The Bliss Factor- Are you where you need to be?

As human beings we are always moving through life with shifting emotions. There are days when we are happy, there are days when we are sad. There are times when we are lonely and there are times when we are filled with joy. It is human to react differently to our changing situations in life.

Every day of our lives cannot be the same. We would be bored if we constantly felt the emotion of great joy. The time would come when we would not feel that joy, as our reactions would be the same every day of our life.

We can appreciate the days when we are happy because we go through the moments and days in our lives, when we are sad, exhausted, happy, funny, depressed and lonely. But what is our bliss, that point in time when we are filled with joy and we know that we are enjoying the emotion of happiness?

As a creator, poet, artist or writer, we know that our emotions, life experiences get reflected in our work. If we want to produce authentic work that reflects who we are as individuals, we need to be true to who we are as creators. Everything that a writer, poet, and creator makes is filled with his or her emotions, values, beliefs and life experiences. Our minds and lives shape all that we produce as creators.

The Bliss Factor in my opinion is when everything is almost perfect and all that is created during this period is filled with positive creative energy. How would you know that you have found your bliss factor?

In my humble opinion, the period of bliss in your life is when you are where you want to be, doing what you enjoy doing, living with the person you love, working with the people you get along with and enjoying life, you are the master or the mistress of your future.

I am where I need to be in life, doing what I need to be doing at this point of time and interacting as well as spending time with the people who share the same interests as I do, which is writing. Are you where you need to be in life, doing what you want to do and experiencing the creative freedom to express yourself?

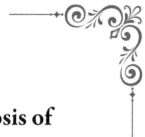

The Metamorphosis of New Writers

Writers are constantly changing and evolving like a bowl of brilliant colours mixing to form new shapes, new ideas, of greater brilliance, creativity and imagination.

Have you experienced the joy of having completed a literary piece and publishing it successfully on a publishing platform? You know that familiar feeling, especially when there is a lovely photograph to accompany your story. Your presentation looks so professional with a complete story, an illustration that gives form and shape to your thought, that mere idea that was floating in the breeze and which you captured to create this literary piece. That is the same feeling that every new writer feels at the beginning of their writing journey.

I will let you in on a little secret. Even after having written so many poems, stories, and articles over the past few years, I still get that same feeling of joy at having published a piece of work. The feeling of using your imagination to create something of literary value to share with the world, is the best reward any writer can receive in life.

A new writer does not always remain a new writer. He or she is constantly evolving. Every new writer goes through the writer's stages of metamorphosis. The writer begins as a novice, just dipping his or her toes into the literary world of writing fiction or non-fiction. The writer is nervous, unsure if the work produced will be enjoyed or ridiculed. The new writer studies the works of other writers to see what works and what does not work. The writer is changing every day into a better writer, as she or he keeps learning the art and craft of writing.

The metamorphosis of a writer continues and does not stop. The new writer will one day evolve to the stage of a seasoned writer, when he or she is able to handle any topic with confidence. This confidence only comes once a writer has found his or her voice as a writer. The writer has developed a unique style and signature that his or her readers recognize.

A brilliant writer can change his or her voice, style, and presentation in his or her writings. This is hard to achieve in one lifetime and we can only hope that we can come close to this level of literary expertise. The metamorphosis of a writer continues throughout life. Learning the art and the wonderful craft of writing never stops, it keeps evolving.

Every writer needs to keep writing constantly, discovering who they are as individuals and the message they want to share with the world. It is true that our writings reflect who we are as individuals, this is one skill that tears away all the masks and the identities we wear as we live our lives in our different roles of father, brother, mother sister, husband, son, or daughter. The day that you stop writing is the day when you stop your evolution as a writer. Write your thoughts and share them every day and you will ultimately evolve to become the writer; you were born to be in life.

Every Day is An Amazing Day

Even when things don't go your way
    An amazing day is every day.
But that is impossible you will say.
We all have days that are fabulous,
And there are ones we would rather forget.
Whatever the day may always bring,
It is a day filled with imagination.
How could a bad day be an amazing day?
It shows us that life has its shadows,
With its darkness and its closed doors.
It also offers us a way filled with hope,
This enables us to grow and cope.
On a good day, we are bathed in the light,
Where we feel so radiant and so bright.
Every day is an amazing and fabulous day,
Enjoy it, appreciate it before it goes away.
We entered this life for all that it offers,
Its joys, its sorrows, its happiness, and its fears.
Just as a bad day can hurt, harm, and injure,
A good day will help you to endure.
A bad day will try to break you down,
A good day will raise you from the ground.
An amazing day may build, or it may destroy,

Worship every day for its lessons and its joy.

Living life without a care

It was the weekend once again,
　　The best time of the week,
He was alive and free once again.
It was the best moment in time,
When he could live his life,
On the rough and on the edge,
Living on a precipitous ledge.
The weekend was when he,
Raced his bike across the city,
As he did the most terrifying stunts.
He raced and chased the fastest cars,
He jumped out of speeding trains,
He parachuted from moving planes.
The weekend was when he could let go,
He could live without a care once more.
He did not have anyone in the world,
He had lost his loving wife and his only girl.
Daredevil Mike was alive at the weekend,
He did not need anyone to comfort him,
Or a shoulder to lean on and cry on.
Daredevil Mike loved the carefree life,
He could lead at the weekend,
After his job at the post office,
Closed on Friday for the weekend.

The meek and mild mannered,
Post office clerk smiling faced Mike,
Would transform into an action man,
Enjoying every minute of his adventurous plan.
Parkour from rooftop to rooftop,
Was his special ability and skill.
Daredevil Mike could leap and roll,
Along the sides of buildings and walls,
He jumped and ran like a panther,
He glided across rooftops and stalls,
He was the undisputed King of Parkour,
Growing faster and stronger every hour.
The weekend would come to an end,
Just as all good things do.
Monday came around the moving bend,
He was back at the Post Office, his old friend.
Sometimes there is no time to stop and stare
While living a reckless life without a care.

Writer's Note: This poem is inspired by my love of Parkour and daredevil stuff. I love action and adventure and wish I could do all those dangerous and daring stunts, like Daredevil Mike. Perhaps in another parallel world, the daredevil version of me is living a life filled with stunts, action and adventure. This is one reason why I enjoy all the action movies like Mission Impossible, Die Hard, Lethal Weapon and the Fast & Furious series.

She Blossomed like a Flower

She returned from India,
    All spiritual and filled with the divine,
She felt she could turn water into wine.
She returned from the trip around the world,
Transformed into a woman from a simple girl.
Equipped with the mystic arts of the East,
She could tame the fiercest and wildest beast,
While preparing a tasty eastern feast.
All the asanas and the poses were great,
Her breathwork and breathing or Pranayama,
Were all focussed and not a minute too late.
She could concentrate her gaze or Drishti,
As she moved her mind over mountain and sea.
Every morning she saluted the regal Sun,
With her special Vinyasa style yoga pose,
She blossomed like a dew kissed rose.
She never forgot her Ujjayi or inhaling,
Using the nose for her exhaling.
She got all her poses perfect and right.
Some poses would give you a fright,
From the upward facing dog,
To the downward facing dog.
At the end of it all she would,

Flop down and sleep like a log.
Her poses of Chaturanga and Savasana,
Were all performed to absolute perfection.
In yoga, the asanas she needed no direction,
She excelled in focus and dynamic meditation.
This powered her success in life every day,
She ended with a thank you to the divine,
With her heartfelt and sincere "Namaste".
Every day that girl blossomed like a Flower
With her special and awesome Yoga Power.

She was in chains where she stood

S hackled and in chains she stood,
    Her heart had turned into hard wood.
She tried to break those chains,
As much as she possibly could.
She was their prisoner where she stood,
It was a prison no one else understood.
The burdens, the customs and the beliefs,
All gave her no freedom or relief.
Bound she was to society's chains,
In all seasons, summer, winters, and rains.
Life was moving faster, round and round,
Like a turntable with a hideous sound.
She was shackled by these chains of gold,
Like a slave she was by society sold.
Those chains of silver, platinum and gold,
Were heavy, hard and metallic cold.
Then one day she saw in her mind,
The chance to live once again,
To be free to fly from a life unkind.
It was an opportunity for her to be,
Free from the shackles of her old destiny.
As she looked at the chains at her feet,
They dissolved like wisps of grey smoke.

Those chains were all the lies and old norms,
The archaic customs to which she was bound.
Those chains of gold evaporated in the light,
They never appeared in her sight.
That girl was now safe, and always free,
To become the woman, she was meant to be.
Shackled and in chains she no longer stood,
Her heart was warm and not made of wood.
Her soul was as free as a bird to fly,
To the stratosphere above the sky.
The dark clouds cleared, and she could see,
The road of opportunities to her new destiny.

Symphony of his Love

S he awoke to the sunlight of a new day,
  Her love had come to finally stay,
It was always to be by her side,
She did not need to run or hide.
He embraced her in his broad arms,
He was smitten by her lovely charms.
There was no better place for her love,
It was her gift from up above.
He held her close to his chest,
In the cold rain and summer heat,
Till their hearts formed one beat.
They were in love so rare,
A love so real beyond compare.
She did not need to become someone,
He loved her in moonlight and in the Sun.
He shrouded her with his warm love,
Their dance was an eloquent romance.
Everything he did was done with love,
A love that they both understood,
A love that was warm, pure and good.
He kept her warm in the coldest night,
He hugged her when she shivered in fright.
He nursed her to health when she was feverish and cool,
He was her friend, her lover, and her romantic fool.

His words and actions were a symphony of his love,
Their orchestra played the sweetest melodies,
That wafted over rooftops, mountains, and trees.
Their children were an orchestra of their romance,
Their love was a playful and passionate dance.
He held her close to his chest,
In snowy winters and summer heat,
Till their hearts formed one beat.
They were in love so simple and rare,
A love so real and alive beyond compare.
She awoke to the sunlight of a brand-new dawn,
Every day their love was reignited and reborn.

How would you use the gift of time?

In a world where anything is possible and the impossible is now possible. What would you do, when it was possible to have an abundance of time? Time as we know it has always been limited and we live our fragile lives withing this mortal framework of hours, minutes and seconds. Time is such a precious element of our human existence and yet we take it for granted and squander it at any chance we get. Save your time and use it well, it is not a commodity you can buy or sell.

If time was available in limitless quantities and we could use it to live our lives to the fullest, what would you do? Would a man or a woman spend more time falling in love and keeping that love, to cherish it for years, or would love be treated like a toy, to be toyed with and discarded, like a rag doll. Romance and love will always be the foundation of civilizations in history.

If there was no limit to the time we could live and enjoy in our earthly existence, we would naturally have to be immortals of some type. If life ceased to be a march towards the dreary end, would we take full advantage of all that life can offer or would we just waste every day? A complete and fulfilled human existence will make us whole, and the grave is not the goal.

If time was infinite for humanity to enjoy, perhaps we could travel into the far reaches of outer space, knowing that it would be possible. If time was limitless for every human being, we would have generations of a family all living and enjoying the wonders of civilization at the same time. Limitless time would make us pioneers, eager to travel beyond our celestial spheres.

If time was limitless, we would be immortals and we would be like tiny human Gods on this world. The concept of the afterlife would cease to exist, if an individual could never die. Time is limited at present, due to our mortal state of being. The knowledge of the cosmos and the keys to eternity would be the miracles of our new humanity.

If your time was limitless in this world from tomorrow, would you live your life in a different way or ways? It would be possible for you to live a hundred lives, to fall in and out of love a thousand times, to spend time with generations of your family, to take up a hundred professions and to maximize your human potential for all eternity. Would an abundance of time be a blessing or a curse, only time will tell? Cherish your time and use it well, it is not yet a commodity that you can buy or sell. In the future you could have a hundred clocks that ring and chime, like a musical orchestra and a windchime.

She was trapped in a Picture

It was the most beautiful painting,
That I had ever seen in my entire life.
It was so beautiful and captivating.
The woman in that picture frame,
Had a very special and lovely smile.
I wondered if that magical smile,
Was for the person in front of her?
Was it for someone she was thinking of,
In her loving heart that day?
If I could just hear her speak,
I am sure she would have a lot to say.
She was the most beautiful captive,
That I had ever seen in a golden frame.
She was gorgeous, she looked elegant,
She was the mystery woman with no name.
The woman in that frame was captive,
To that moment locked away in time,
To that memory frozen in space.
Her love was captive in that frame,
As it illuminated her pretty face,
As she posed in silk, cotton and lace.
I hope that she had found her romance and love,
That her life was filled with love in every way,

That she was free to love and be loved every day.

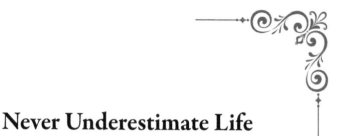

Never Underestimate Life

L ife has so many unexpected surprises. People can surprise you. You can also surprise yourself. We all tend to underestimate ourselves, other people and the events that take place in life. Some people are capable of doing so much although others put little faith and trust in them.

When negative things happen in life, we feel that we will fall under its effects, yet we surprise ourselves when we can adapt, change and rise up from failures. The world was broken and crushed after the pandemic, yet two years later humanity is coming back stronger.

Lives have been lost and lives have been changed after the pandemic and the war in Ukraine, yet people will return to their lives. People will rebuild their homes and bring back life to some type of normality.

Never underestimate your skills and abilities in life to do so much. You are capable of change and you are able to push the boundaries of your life and achieve so much more in life. You will surprise yourself if you just decide to make the required changes to experience and shape a new destiny.

I was watching a Japanese program yesterday about young children, between the ages of two to four, who do tasks for their parents. The young children achieve and triumph in the chores that they were given and they realize that their work is important. Japanese culture focuses on children being independent and self-reliant.

Never underestimate your abilities to bring about changes to your life, your environment, and the lives of others. Change does scare everyone, whether we want to accept it or not, yet change is necessary as it helps us to grow stronger in life. Never underestimate the abilities of others to make positive changes in the world. Give people, yourself, and the world a chance to surprise you and you will realize that there is so much potential and changes taking place around you because we are all agents of positive change.

Puppet on a plane

The passengers sat in their seats,
Moving and swaying in their seats,
Like puppets with a secret puppeteer,
Making them smile, move, and peer.
He felt like a puppet on a plane,
So pleased that he was airborne again.
That damn virus was so deadly,
It was not going away at any time,
That was less than likely.
She felt like a puppet on a plane,
Hoping that it was safe to fly.
She just wanted to feel safe once again,
As safe as can be on a sealed plane.
Were they all puppets on this plane,
Would a virus attack them again?
By that unknown virus mutation?
The passengers hoped and prayed,
That all those tests and vaccines,
Had protected them all on the plane,
From any new variant or mutation.
The children and families were happy again,
They sat feeling safe like puppets on a plane,
Happy to vacation and visit family once again.
Published in Medium on 19/01/2022

Puppet on a train

It was back to travelling once again,
 He was just another puppet on a train.
Things were back to normal once again,
Working in summer, spring and rain.
He got off at his station,
He opened his umbrella in the rain.
The streets were very busy once again,
All the puppets walked in the rain.
Life was normal from India to Spain.
The offices were crowded once again,
It was back to losses and income gain.
The economy is on the rise,
Bringing tears to a puppet's eyes.
The trudge to work and home,
The freedom to freely roam,
Is back in the world once again.
The puppet was going back home,
After another day at the office,
Trading currency and lives like fish.
The life of the puppet is normal again.
Freedom to do as the world pleases,
Was the destiny of the puppet in the rain.
It was filled with happiness, joy and pain.
There goes another puppet on a train,

Back at work and walking in the rain.

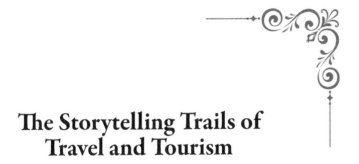

The Storytelling Trails of Travel and Tourism

Travel stories are always very exciting to hear and some of the best storytellers are those who travel to the most exotic places in the world. Every place visited by a tourist has a story waiting to be told. There are so many tourists visiting new and interesting locations in the world.

Thanks to social media, tourists are now travel storytellers, telling the world their stories through articles, blog posts, pictures on Instagram and in travel videos on YouTube. With the advent of immersive technology, it is now possible for an armchair traveller to have a more exhilarating experience of any country in the world, with the help of artificial intelligence and virtual reality 360-degree videos.

I vividly recall the images, sights and sounds of the last trip I made with family and friends to the Hill Station in Darjeeling, India. This is a travel story that was a wonderful experience and a fascinating experience. The visit to the tea plantations, the settlements as we moved to the top of the mountain to reach Darjeeling which is located in the Himalayas, was memorable.

https://youtu.be/D-PxV8BJF8s

Another, spectacular moment was when we visited Margaret's Deck, the tea lounge was a grand feeling as we absorbed the remarkable views of the Himalayan Mountain range close by. Margaret's Deck appears to be suspended, as it was built jutting out from the side of the mountain side. This tea-lounge is definitely a place worth visiting, when in India.

https://youtu.be/dQ2eKRbW844

As you will notice in this article, I have taken the reader into the experience of travelling to a far and distant land, by simply narrating my travel to one tourist spot in India. Similarly, travel writers and tourists are Storytellers, who share their experiences with the readers of the world. If you happen to be a travel writer as well as a photographer, you are also a Storyteller serving society stories through your articles, poetry, stories and videos. Orla Kenny is one such Travel Storyteller, who shares her wonderful articles and photographs of her travels for readers to enjoy.

Let the Skies Hold Your Dreams- Let it rain its Miracles

We sleep and we dream.
This life is so much more,
To us, it does sometimes seem.
We love, we work, we love,
We pray, we play with our lives,
Seeking help from the Gods above.
We wish that life changes for us,
To something bigger and better.
We hope that our dreams come true,
Bigger, better, and so much brighter.
We send up our wishes to the stars,
We wish we had cosmic powers.
Let the skies hold all your dreams.
Let every wish you make on a star,
Increase in its power every hour.
Let your wishes resound in space,
As every star shines in its place.
Doubt and regret lose their power,
As belief in magic increases every hour.
Let the skies hold all your dreams,
Life is mystical it always seems.
Bring all the power and your skills,

To bring rainfall and miracles.
Let the skies hold all your dreams,
While your life embraces miracles.

The Pillars of Creation

P illars of gas extend out into the cosmos,
    Like the fingers of Gods, they appear.
Large hands reaching out,
They rise, they fall and disappear.
A telescope catches this spectacle,
Of beauty in the depths of space.
A celestial display filled with mystery,
Dance and rise in perfect harmony.
The pillars of creation,
Are magnificent displays of cosmic force.
The fingers of the Gods extend into space,
Shaping worlds through time and space.
These cosmic gases arise in celestial displays,
In magical performance every soul reveres,
Existing in space for 60 to 70 light years.
We are fortunate to have seen,
These marvels called the pillars of creation.
That rise, fall and disappear in isolation.

Author's Note: The Pillars of Creation refers to the photograph taken by the Hubble Telescope of elephant trunks of interstellar gas and dust in the Eagle Nebula, which is about 6500 to 7000 light years away in space.

Writing Prompt- Do you believe that you have lived before?

There have been times when I have felt something familiar about a place or an object. It is almost as if I have been there at some time in my life, yet I have never visited the place before. Though now with the internet and everything online, it could be that I had caught a glimpse of a place or an object online, it is a possibility and cannot be ruled out, this sense of déjà vu.

I have also had the feeling of having met a person before, although I am meeting them for the very first time. There was a soul connection when I met my wife and life partner. I love watching movies set during different historical periods, a few of them being Victorian and Mediaeval England, ancient Egypt, mediaeval China and the period of the early pioneers and settlers in America. I love these periods and it could be because I grew up watching these movies.

According to several articles online, I could be one of those individuals who have lived past lives. Are your Past Lives, Fact, Fiction, Fairy Tales or a Wonderful Fascinating Fantasy of Deception?

A few of the signs that may suggest that you have been reincarnated are given below:

- Recurring dreams of places or periods or incidences.
- A soul connection with a person.
- A sense of Deja-vu of having visited a place before or having

done something before, that you are doing for the very first
time.

- A birthmark on a particular part of the part, where an injury
  could have occurred in a past life.
- An ache in a part of the body, that occurs without any reason,
  could indicate a physical trauma in a past life.
- An affinity for certain time-periods in history, could suggest
  that you were from that period and have lived during that
  time.
- A feeling that you do not belong to Earth, could be the result
  of being reborn several times and you are bored with the way
  humans live on Earth and wish to break the cycle.
- The ability to understand and speak a foreign language
  without difficulty, could suggest having lived a past life or
  lives.
- A phobia in this life could suggest a trauma that occurred in a
  past life.

These are just some of the signs that you or someone you know
could have lived before and been reincarnated. What do you think?
Is this the result of an overactive imagination or could it be true?
Whatever the fact may be, the myths related to reincarnation have been
around for years and still exist today in the 21st century. Write a story,
article or poem related to this prompt, "Do you believe that you have
lived before?"

Don't miss out!

Visit the website below and you can sign up to receive emails whenever Warren Brown publishes a new book. There's no charge and no obligation.

https://books2read.com/r/B-A-LFGF-YOSQC

Connecting independent readers to independent writers.

Did you love *Ocean of Ideas and Inspiration for Writers*? Then you should read *Castle of Ideas and Inspiration for Writers*[1] by Warren Brown!

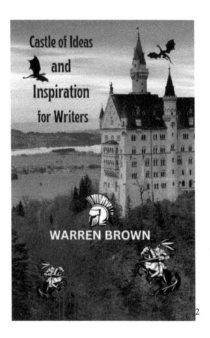

"The Castle of Ideas and Inspiration for Writers", is composed of a collection of essays, stories and poems. Each creative literary piece will inspire you to create your own collection of writings. Each story is a writing prompt for you to start creating your literary work.

This castle is filled with stories and poems on a variety of issues, including essays on how you can become a better creative writer. The subjects covered in this collection will open your eyes, to your own imagination and creativity.

After reading just a few pages of this book, you will be inspired by the "idea keys" contained within its pages to write and keep writing.

---

1. https://books2read.com/u/4EJdqo

2. https://books2read.com/u/4EJdqo

You will find that your Muse will be awakened and your mind will get new ideas. Every title of a chapter in this book is a "key" for you to use and develop into your creative work.

Writing is a non-stop process and it takes time and effort. Great writers are not born, it is only with inspiration and dedication to the literary craft that they develop into notable writers. You may not win the Pulitzer Prize or the Nobel Prize for Literature, but you will write and gift your literary creations to the world.

What will you discover within the walls of this great castle? You will discover new ideas, perspectives, inspiration and creativity, that are the bricks and mortar of your imagination for building your own literary castle.

Read more at https://warren4.wixsite.com/warren.

Also by Warren Brown

Prolific Writing for Everyone
Universe of Creativity and Inspiration for Writers
Ocean of Ideas and Inspiration for Writers
On Writing Magic
The Writer's Creativity Cave
The Writer's Oasis
Castle of Ideas and Inspiration for Writers
Chasm of Creativity and Inspiration For Writers
Island of Creativity and Inspiration for Writers

Standalone
Supernova: A Collection of Science Fiction Short Stories
Instant Poetry App
The Power of the Storyteller- A Collection of Short Stories
Vintage Tales: Eurasian Short Stories
Impostor Assassin
Camelot Crypto 1- Crypto Genesis
Camelot Crypto 2- Crypto Odyssey
Camelot Crypto 3- Crypto Symbiosis
Camelot Crypto: Three Short Crypto-currency Stories
Three Christmas Coins: A Poem
The Christmas Dimension

Watch for more at https://warren4.wixsite.com/warren.

About the Author

Warren Brown is an Author who has written in several genres from fiction to non-fiction. Warren is a certified Life Coach and Hypnotherapist. Warren completed his Advertising and Copywriting training through American Writers and Artists Inc. (AWAI). I have been an Indie publisher for over eleven years now. I have been writing and publishing on the web since 1993. Website:

https://warren4.wixsite.com/warren

Medium:

https://warrenauthor.medium.com/

Substack:

https://warrenbrown.substack.com/

Read more at https://warren4.wixsite.com/warren.

Milton Keynes UK
Ingram Content Group UK Ltd.
UKHW010931231123
433129UK00001B/128